Grade 3

Scott Foresman
Weekly Tests

Glenview, Illinois • Boston, Massachusetts • Chandler, Arizona • Upper Saddle River, New Jersey

D0902856

Copyright © Pearson Education, Inc., or its affiliates. All Rights Reserved. Printed in the United States of America. This publication is protected by copyright, and permission should be obtained from the publisher prior to any prohibited reproduction, storage in a retrieval system, or transmission in any form or by any means, electronic, mechanical, photocopying, recording, or likewise. The publisher hereby grants permission to reproduce these pages, in part or in whole, for classroom use only, the number not to exceed the number of students in each class. Notice of copyright must appear on all copies. For information regarding permissions, write to Pearson Curriculum Group Rights & Permissions, One Lake Street, Upper Saddle River, New Jersey 07458.

Pearson, Scott Foresman, and Pearson Scott Foresman are trademarks, in the U.S. and/or other countries, of Pearson Education, Inc., or its affiliates.

ISBN-13: 978-0-328-50879-2
ISBN-10:   0-328-50879-9

3 4 5 6 7 8 9 10 V016 18 17 16 15 14 13 12 11 10

CONTENTS

Unit 1 Living and Learning

Unit 2 Smart Solutions

Unit 3 People and Nature

Unit 4 One of a Kind

3 Copyright © Pearson Education, Inc., or its affiliates. All Rights Reserved.

Unit 5 Cultures

Unit 6 Freedom

3 Copyright © Pearson Education, Inc., or its affiliates. All Rights Reserved.

VOCABULARY

Directions

Find the word or words with the same meaning as the underlined word. Fill in the circle next to the answer.

1 We are going to see a <u>bat</u> exhibit at the zoo.

○ an object used to hit a ball
○ beginning
○ fluttering
○ a small mammal

2 The class president serves a <u>term</u> of one year.

○ a word or phrase
○ dinner
○ period of time
○ report

3 The wind <u>blew</u> in the ship's sails.

○ gusted
○ lost
○ covered
○ rocked

4 Tim charged the <u>battery</u> so he could use it for his flashlight.

○ power user
○ power source
○ light bulb
○ three pack

5 They <u>plug</u> the hole with mud to keep out squirrels.

○ open
○ close
○ paint
○ water

6 His <u>vision</u> is better when he wears his glasses.

○ visor
○ hearing
○ tasting
○ eyesight

7 When the <u>fuel</u> goes into the tank, the car will run.

○ stuff used to pay for things
○ stuff used to clean things out
○ material used to power and make things work
○ material used to cover and hide things

3 Copyright © Pearson Education, Inc., or its affiliates. All Rights Reserved.

GO ON

PHONICS

Directions
Find the word that best answers each question. Fill in the circle next to the answer.

8 Colette put the apples she picked in a <u>basket</u>.

Which word has the same syllable pattern as the <u>VC/CV</u> in <u>basket</u>?

- ○ accord
- ○ crime
- ○ music
- ○ third

9 We made cinnamon <u>bread</u> with Grandpa.

Which word has the same short vowel sound as the <u>ea</u> in <u>bread</u>?

- ○ beauty
- ○ ready
- ○ beach
- ○ team

10 She tapped her <u>pencil</u> on the table.

Which word has the same syllable pattern as the <u>VC/CV</u> in <u>pencil</u>?

- ○ picnic
- ○ planet
- ○ placed
- ○ second

11 Take the time to <u>tell</u> us all about your trip.

Which word has the same short vowel sound as the <u>e</u> in <u>tell</u>?

- ○ meet
- ○ meat
- ○ met
- ○ mate

12 Things <u>happen</u> whenever Emma gets an idea.

Which word has the same syllable pattern as the <u>VC/CV</u> in <u>happen</u>?

- ○ catching
- ○ lower
- ○ seven
- ○ lesson

COMPREHENSION

Brighter School Days

Roy and Sammy rode their bikes to school. They rode through the gates and saw the new solar roof on top of the school. The morning sun was already shining on it.

Last week in school, Roy and Sammy learned about the sun's energy. They also learned about how a solar roof uses the sun's energy. The sun shines all day onto

GO ON

3 Copyright © Pearson Education, Inc., or its affiliates. All Rights Reserved.

solar cells on the roof. The solar cells take in and save energy from the sun. This energy is used for lights in the school.

Sammy parked his bike. He said, "Look, Roy, there's the new solar roof we helped our dads put up on the school. We carried lots of tools for them so they could go up to the roof. Too bad the kids couldn't go up."

"I know," replied Roy as he got off his bike. He added, "But it was cool riding in the crane with our dads."

"Look," said Sammy, "there's a leaf on one of the solar cells. Let's get a ladder and take it off so that it doesn't block the sun. And we can see if the cells are working."

Sammy ran behind the school to look for a ladder. As he followed Sammy, Roy said, "I'm not sure that's a good idea."

Tools and ladders were still in the schoolyard. The boys started to look for a ladder they could carry. "What are you boys up to?" said a voice from behind them.

The boys turned around to see Mr. Harris, the school groundskeeper. He walked towards them with a hammer in his hand. "We were just looking for a ladder to check the solar roof and get a leaf off," said Roy.

Mr. Harris looked at them and said, "Come with me."

Sammy and Roy followed Mr. Harris into the school and down to the basement. He brought them to a room with a box on the wall. Circles with numbers on them turned on the box. Mr. Harris explained that the numbers were the energy readings. The solar cells on the roof were taking in the sun's energy. Mr. Harris added, "When the lights in your classroom are turned on, they use this energy. As long as there is a sun, we will not run out."

"But what about the leaf?" wondered Sammy. "It's blocking the sun! We need a ladder to get to the roof!"

Mr. Harris answered, "The wind will probably blow it off. But I have an idea if you are interested in the solar roof. Would you both like to check on the energy readings every week?"

Both boys nodded their heads yes. "Great!" said Mr. Harris. "Well, let's get you to your class so your teacher knows where you are." He walked the boys to their classroom.

When they got there, Mr. Harris told their teacher, "It looks like these boys have a bright future in school." They all chuckled.

3 Copyright © Pearson Education, Inc., or its affiliates. All Rights Reserved.

Directions

Choose the item that best answers each question about the selection you just read.
Fill in the circle next to the answer.

13 When does this story most likely take place?

- ○ on a spring morning
- ○ in the middle of winter
- ○ during summer vacation
- ○ during the evening in autumn

14 Which best describes Sammy?

- ○ lazy
- ○ sad
- ○ curious
- ○ grumpy

15 What did Sammy want to do that he knew he should not?

- ○ go onto the solar roof
- ○ carry tools to his dad
- ○ ride Roy's bike
- ○ take Mr. Harris's hammer

16 Based on the story, how do you know that Roy usually goes along with what Sammy decides to do?

- ○ Sammy is smarter than Roy.
- ○ Sammy is like an older brother to Roy.
- ○ Roy thinks Sammy has a good idea to go up on the solar roof.
- ○ Roy helps look for a ladder even though he thinks it is not a good idea.

17 How did the boys almost get into trouble at school?

- ○ They almost rode their bikes to school.
- ○ They almost rode through the wrong school gate.
- ○ They almost went into the basement.
- ○ They almost climbed onto the solar roof.

18 Why did Mr. Harris take the boys to the basement?

- ○ to put away his hammer
- ○ to get a ladder for them to go to the roof
- ○ to show them that the solar roof was working
- ○ to get them some water

19 How did Sammy and Roy stay out of trouble?

- ○ Mr. Harris chased them away from the tools in the schoolyard.
- ○ Mr. Harris showed them how to check the solar cells without going on the roof.
- ○ Mr. Harris let Sammy and Roy go onto the roof to get the leaf off.
- ○ Their dads had to come to school to fix the solar roof.

20 Which sentence tells the theme of the story?

- ○ Adults spoil everything.
- ○ The sun is very powerful.
- ○ You can learn about something without getting in trouble.
- ○ It does not pay to be curious.

GO ON

3 Copyright © Pearson Education, Inc., or its affiliates. All Rights Reserved.

WRITTEN RESPONSE TO THE SELECTION

Look Back and Write Look back at the question on page 29. Think about how Charlie acts when the power first goes out and what he does later in the story. Now write a paragraph explaining the changes in Charlie's behavior.

The information in the box below will help you remember what you should think about when you write your composition.

REMEMBER—YOU SHOULD

☐ explain the changes in Charlie's behavior after the power goes out.

☐ include details from the story to support your ideas.

☐ make sure that your ideas about Charlie are clear so that the reader understands what you are saying.

☐ try to use correct spelling, capitalization, punctuation, grammar, and sentences.

3 Copyright © Pearson Education, Inc., or its affiliates. All Rights Reserved.

_____

_____

_____

_____

_____

_____

_____

_____

_____

_____

_____

_____

_____

_____

_____

_____

_____

_____

_____

_____

_____

_____

3 Copyright © Pearson Education, Inc., or its affiliates. All Rights Reserved.

VOCABULARY

Directions

Find the word or words with the same meaning as the underlined word. Fill in the circle next to the answer.

1 There was <u>plenty</u> to eat at the fair.

○ nothing
○ much
○ little
○ enough

2 Sam's dog kept <u>straying</u>.

○ barking
○ digging
○ whining
○ wandering

3 The <u>marketplace</u> was filled with people.

○ movie theater
○ parking lot
○ shopping area
○ playing field

4 Toni did not have the <u>knowledge</u> to finish the project.

○ understanding
○ time
○ equipment
○ money

5 The <u>carpetmaker</u> hired an assistant.

○ fisherman
○ manager
○ storyteller
○ rug weaver

6 Paul used a different color <u>thread</u>.

○ string
○ paper
○ crayon
○ paint

7 The <u>merchant</u> was always busy.

○ carpenter
○ shopkeeper
○ news reporter
○ farmer

GO ON

3 Copyright © Pearson Education, Inc., or its affiliates. All Rights Reserved.

WORD ANALYSIS

Directions

Find the correct plural form of the underlined word. Fill in the circle next to the answer.

8 Dora's <u>juice</u> spilled onto the table.

- ⚪ juices
- ⚪ juises
- ⚪ juicy
- ⚪ juicies

9 Jorge gave his cat a <u>dish</u> of milk.

- ⚪ dush
- ⚪ dishs
- ⚪ dishies
- ⚪ dishes

10 The salesman asked, "Is your <u>family</u> from out of town?"

- ⚪ families
- ⚪ familyes
- ⚪ familys
- ⚪ famillies

11 Tim was paid one <u>penny</u> for each empty can he found.

- ⚪ pennys
- ⚪ pennyes
- ⚪ pennies
- ⚪ penns

12 Billy made a <u>wish</u> before blowing out his birthday candles.

- ⚪ wishs
- ⚪ wishes
- ⚪ wishys
- ⚪ wishies

COMPREHENSION

A Kid Kids a Pig

Early spring on the farm was a time when the animals liked to be outside. They loved to spend time with each other after the long, cold winter.

This spring there was a new kid in town. A kid is what you call a baby goat. This kid went by the name of Gabby Goat. She just loved to tease the other animals on the farm. "Oh, that Gabby Goat is quite a kidder," everyone would say.

The favorite target of Gabby Goat's kidding was young Snortin Pig. Snortin loved putting his piggy nose into the mud and then snorting it out. Gabby Goat teased, "Snortin Pig's nose is a flat, big, muddy nose of a pig!"

Snortin didn't mind the teasing. He knew that Gabby was doing it in fun. Snortin

3 Copyright © Pearson Education, Inc., or its affiliates. All Rights Reserved.

GO ON

would laugh after her jokes. He'd say, "I know my nose is flat. How about that?" Gabby Goat would then giggle and say, "I have the perfect nose of a kid. It's not too small and not too big."

This happy kidding around went on all spring and into the summer. One day late in July, Gabby Goat found the tree where the buzzing bees made their honey. Unable to resist sweet honey, she put her nose into the tree to have just a tiny taste.

Angrily the bees came buzzing out, and one stung Gabby Goat right on her nose. "Ouch!" she cried and ran to Snortin Pig's pen to cool her perfect nose in his mud.

Snortin took one look at Gabby's face and laughed, "Gabby Goat, look at how your nose just grows and grows!" She was so upset she just stuck her tongue out at Snortin Pig and ran right home.

Hootin Owl watched all this happen from high in his tree. Mr. Owl had been watching Gabby Goat tease Snortin Pig and the other farm animals since early spring. He flew to Gabby's pen and wisely said, "Gabby Goat, don't dish it out if you can't take it too! Don't laugh at others if you don't want them to laugh at you."

Directions

Choose the item that best answers each question about the selection you just read. Fill in the circle next to the answer.

3 Copyright © Pearson Education, Inc., or its affiliates. All Rights Reserved.

13 **Why did the farm animals like the early spring?**

○ They could be outside before the long, hot summer.

○ They could be outside after the long, cold winter.

○ They could tease each other.

○ They could be outside after the short, hot winter.

14 **What would Snortin Pig do after putting his nose into the mud?**

○ He would ask for a tissue.

○ He would start to sneeze.

○ He would get upset.

○ He would snort it out.

GO ON

15 What would Snortin Pig and Gabby Goat do after she teased him?

○ Snortin Pig would laugh, and Gabby Goat would giggle.

○ Snortin Pig would cry, and Gabby Goat would run home.

○ Snortin Pig would laugh, and Gabby Goat would eat honey.

○ Snortin Pig would sit in the mud, and Gabby Goat would watch.

16 When did Gabby Goat find the honey tree?

○ late in July

○ early in spring

○ during the long, dark winter

○ after she got stung on the nose

17 What did Gabby Goat do right after she was stung on the nose?

○ She ran right home.

○ She put her nose in the tree to eat some honey.

○ She put it in Snortin Pig's cool mud.

○ She teased Snortin Pig.

18 Who talks to Gabby Goat at the end of the story?

○ Snortin Pig

○ Buzzing Bees

○ Hootin Owl

○ another character

19 Why did Hootin Owl fly to Gabby Goat's pen?

○ He couldn't mind his own business.

○ He wanted to help her learn to be a better friend.

○ He wanted to find out which tree had the honey.

○ He wanted to tattle on her.

20 Which character lets you know the moral of this fable?

○ Gabby Goat

○ Hootin Owl

○ Snortin Pig

○ the stinging bee

3   Copyright © Pearson Education, Inc., or its affiliates. All Rights Reserved.

GO ON

WRITTEN RESPONSE TO THE SELECTION

Look Back and Write The merchant's daughter is important in the story. Look back at pages 73–74. Then explain how she influences the end of the story. Provide evidence from the selection to support your answer.

The information in the box below will help you remember what you should think about when you write your composition.

REMEMBER—YOU SHOULD

☐ explain how the merchant's daughter influences the end of the story.

☐ use details from the story as the evidence to support your answer.

☐ make sure that each action you describe is in its proper order or sequence.

☐ try to use correct spelling, capitalization, punctuation, grammar, and sentences.

3 Copyright © Pearson Education, Inc., or its affiliates. All Rights Reserved.

GO ON

3 Copyright © Pearson Education, Inc., or its affiliates. All Rights Reserved.

VOCABULARY

Directions

Find the word or words with the same meaning as the underlined word. Fill in the circle next to the answer.

1 Jim saw the cat's tail <u>twitch</u> as it watched a bird.

○ wave hello
○ make small, jerky movements
○ remain motionless
○ move in slow motion

2 Their camping <u>gear</u> protected them.

○ collection of photographs and paintings
○ metal parts on a bicycle
○ equipment needed for an activity
○ food and drink

3 She liked to sit under the <u>willow</u>.

○ a type of tree with narrow, long branches
○ a type of yellow, shiny rock
○ a rain cloud
○ a porch swing

4 Keith <u>yanked</u> open the heavy door.

○ pulled with a sudden movement
○ pushed with a gentle movement
○ kicked with the feet
○ was unable to move

5 James and his family had a <u>splendid</u> vacation.

○ long and tiring
○ scary and frightening
○ terrible and unhappy
○ great and excellent

6 Wear your <u>parka</u> when you go out.

○ two-piece swimsuit
○ warm, heavy jacket with a hood
○ wrap-around sunglasses
○ ladies' flip-flop sandals

3 Copyright © Pearson Education, Inc., or its affiliates. All Rights Reserved.

GO ON

WORD ANALYSIS

Directions
Find the correct form of the underlined word to fill in the blank. Fill in the circle next to the word that fills the blank.

7 Tina did not <u>cry</u> when she went to the doctor, but she _____ when her doll broke.

- ○ cryed
- ○ cried
- ○ cryied
- ○ criyed

8 Jake's <u>hope</u> was to get a new bike for his birthday, but his twin brother was _____ for a baseball bat.

- ○ hooping
- ○ hopping
- ○ hopeing
- ○ hoping

9 Jason's house was not just <u>big</u>, it was _____ than all the other houses on his block.

- ○ biger
- ○ bigyer
- ○ bigger
- ○ biggier

10 If you thought that last comic was <u>funny</u>, you'll think the next one is the _____ ever.

- ○ funniest
- ○ funnyest
- ○ funnest
- ○ funnyiest

11 Mom doesn't need to <u>shop</u> for shoes today because she went _____ yesterday.

- ○ shopeing
- ○ shooping
- ○ shoping
- ○ shopping

12 It _____ Grandma very much that little Tammy remembered to say "<u>please</u>" and "thank you."

- ○ pleaseed
- ○ pleasd
- ○ pleased
- ○ pleasied

3 Copyright © Pearson Education, Inc., or its affiliates. All Rights Reserved.

GO ON

COMPREHENSION

Thomas Alva Edison

Thomas Alva Edison gave the world the electric light. Without him, the world might still be a dark place. But the light was not the only thing he made. He also invented the record player, the movie camera, and more than 1,200 other things. About every two weeks, Edison made something new!

Edison was born in Ohio in 1847. His family moved to Michigan when he was seven years old. Edison went to school for only two months. His mother did teach him a few things because she had been a teacher. But Edison learned a lot by himself. He was very curious as a child.

When he was twelve years old, he got his first job. He became a newsboy on a train. Soon, he set up a lab in a car of the train. He wanted to carry out some tests during his time off. Edison's first job did not end well. He was let go when a fire started on the floor of the train car. Edison then worked at other jobs for the next five years. But he spent much of his time on his ideas for new machines.

Edison got his first patent in 1868 for a machine that helped with voting. In 1870, he made a stock-ticker. A stock-ticker is a machine that prints stock prices on paper. He was then able to build his first shop in New Jersey.

Edison always wanted more time to work. He called himself a "two-shift man." This is because he worked sixteen out of every twenty-four hours. Sometimes he worked so hard that his wife had to tell him to sleep and eat.

Thomas Edison died in 1931 when he was 84. He had made life better for people all over the world.

3 Copyright © Pearson Education, Inc., or its affiliates. All Rights Reserved.

GO ON

COMPREHENSION

Directions
Choose the item that best answers each question about the selection you just read. Fill in the circle next to the answer.

13 What event happened before Edison's family moved to Michigan?

○ Edison invented the electric light.

○ Edison got his first patent.

○ Edison was born in Ohio.

○ Edison worked on a train.

14 Which word best describes Thomas Edison?

○ lazy

○ wicked

○ hard-working

○ alone

15 In what year did Edison get his first patent?

○ 1847

○ 1868

○ 1870

○ 1931

16 What happened soon after Edison got a job on a train?

○ His mother taught him some things.

○ He worked at other jobs.

○ He made a machine that helped with voting.

○ He set up a lab in a train car.

17 Why did Edison call himself a "two-shift man"?

○ because he liked to drive

○ because he worked very hard

○ because he did not go to school

○ because he had two jobs

18 What happened before Edison got his first job?

○ He worked sixteen hours every day.

○ His wife had to tell him to eat and sleep.

○ He left behind many good ideas.

○ He went to school for only two months.

19 Why was Edison let go from his job on the train?

○ A fire started on the floor of his train car.

○ He did not want to work on the train.

○ He was always late for work.

○ He was working at too many jobs.

20 What did Edison do while he was working at other jobs for five years?

○ He set up his first lab on a train car.

○ He invented the stock-ticker.

○ He spent a lot of his time on his ideas for machines.

○ He built his first shop in New Jersey.

3 Copyright © Pearson Education, Inc., or its affiliates. All Rights Reserved.

GO ON

Name _____

WRITTEN RESPONSE TO THE SELECTION

Look Back and Write Look back at the question on page 99. Think about the most important events that happened in the story. Now write a response to the question. Be sure to include details from the story to support your answer.

The information in the box below will help you remember what you should think about when you write your composition.

REMEMBER—YOU SHOULD

☐   explain how events in the story show that people can achieve goals.

☐   describe each event in detail so that the reader understands your composition.

☐   make sure you state your conclusion clearly for the reader.

☐   try to use correct spelling, capitalization, punctuation, grammar, and sentences.

3   Copyright © Pearson Education, Inc., or its affiliates. All Rights Reserved.

3 Copyright © Pearson Education, Inc., or its affiliates. All Rights Reserved.

VOCABULARY

Directions

Find the word or words with the same meaning as the underlined word. Fill in the circle next to the answer.

1 Rita <u>traded</u> her blue crayon for a red one.

- ○ gave away
- ○ sold
- ○ bought
- ○ exchanged

2 This market sells a <u>variety</u> of fruits.

- ○ number of types
- ○ just one type
- ○ bundles
- ○ thousands

3 Meg placed the books on the <u>shelves</u>.

- ○ boxes under a bed for storing things
- ○ horizontal boards for holding things
- ○ cushiony office chairs
- ○ low, long dinner tables

4 I visited the children's <u>section</u> for a book.

- ○ an area of a city
- ○ the front of a building
- ○ the second floor
- ○ a part of something

5 The fruit <u>spoiled</u> after a while.

- ○ tasted yummy
- ○ became ripe
- ○ became not good to eat
- ○ was treated with extra care

6 One of my chores is folding the <u>laundry</u>.

- ○ freshly cleaned clothes
- ○ clothes hanging in the closet
- ○ clothes that no longer fit
- ○ badly torn clothes

3 Copyright © Pearson Education, Inc., or its affiliates. All Rights Reserved.

GO ON

PHONICS

*D*irections
Find the word that best answers each question. Fill in the circle next to the answer.

7 Monday is the day that Jenny <u>cleans</u> her floors.

Which word has the same sound as the <u>ea</u> in <u>cleans</u>?

○ earth
○ clever
○ bear
○ cheese

8 Jessica's hair is so long that her mom likes to <u>braid</u> it.

Which word has the same sound as the <u>ai</u> in <u>braid</u>?

○ fire
○ brand
○ display
○ chair

9 The butterfly seems to <u>float</u> through the air.

Which word has the same sound as the <u>oa</u> in <u>float</u>?

○ cot
○ rope
○ frown
○ stoop

10 Do you <u>agree</u> that four quarters equal one dollar?

Which word has the same sound as the <u>ee</u> in <u>agree</u>?

○ pie
○ dream
○ pet
○ there

11 Sunlight burst through the <u>window</u>.

Which word has the same sound as the <u>ow</u> in <u>window</u>?

○ one
○ coach
○ shower
○ couch

12 I wrote a letter to the <u>mayor</u> of the city.

Which word has the same sound as the <u>ay</u> in <u>mayor</u>?

○ plate
○ right
○ key
○ yard

3 Copyright © Pearson Education, Inc., or its affiliates. All Rights Reserved.

COMPREHENSION

The Vacation Debate

Every year, by the middle of summer, cities across the country become like ovens. In the morning, people go to work tired and hot. Children out of school grow bored. It's time to think about a vacation! But how can you get friends or family to agree on a trip? This guide will help you plan a trip that will please everyone.

Everyone wants to cool off out of town—anywhere out of town. The beach, the mountains, the lake are all great places to go. The *place* is not what people fight about. What people disagree on is *how* to go on vacation.

Some people like camping. Others like to stay in a resort hotel. Both places can be a home-away-from-home. They offer rest at night. But camps and hotels have different styles. Camps bring nature, while hotels bring comfort. Camps are often away from crowds, yet hotels can bring people together. And camps, unlike hotels, can be part of a plan to save money.

Both camps and hotels provide visitors with a break from the city and a chance to cool off. Camps might be near a lake, river, or stream. Most hotels have pools. Both places also offer entertainment—of different kinds. While people at camps might fish or stargaze, hotel visitors might play tennis or watch TV.

Camps and hotels present different types of meals. While camping, people often cook for themselves around a cozy fire. People who stay in hotels usually eat in restaurants.

"I can't stand camping," says Keisha Silver. "All the bugs. And the snakes. Oh, and the bears."

Paul Padilla feels differently. He says, "It doesn't make sense to leave my tiny apartment in the city just to sit around an air-conditioned hotel room watching TV. I need fresh air, stars, the sounds of crickets!"

Whatever you prefer, remember: The point of a vacation is to escape the cares of the world. It can be done on a lawn chair in the park. The best way to plan a vacation is to think about how you relax.

3 Copyright © Pearson Education, Inc., or its affiliates. All Rights Reserved.

GO ON

COMPREHENSION

Directions

Choose the item that best answers each question about the selection you just read.
Fill in the circle next to the answer.

13 What is the author's purpose for writing the selection?

○ to recommend fancy resort hotels

○ to tell people to relax more

○ to guide people on their camping trips

○ to help people plan a successful trip

14 Which of the following is *not* a similarity shared by camps and hotels?

○ They both offer a break from the city.

○ They both have the sounds of crickets.

○ They both give people a chance to cool off.

○ They both can be a home-away-from-home.

15 In which way do camps and hotels differ the most?

○ a place to stay away from home

○ number of ways to relax

○ cost

○ swimming

16 Camps and hotels are similar because

○ they both offer a chance to cool off.

○ they both offer a place away from crowds.

○ they both make everyone comfortable.

○ they both offer a chance to be in nature.

17 Compared to camps, hotels are

○ less friendly.

○ more fun.

○ less comfortable.

○ more expensive.

18 What is the main similarity between camps and hotels?

○ They both have plenty of fresh air.

○ They both cause families to disagree.

○ They are both places to vacation.

○ They are both near bodies of water.

19 What conclusion can you draw about Keisha Silver?

○ She never goes anywhere without air-conditioning.

○ She would enjoy vacationing with Paul Padilla.

○ She never goes camping without bug spray.

○ She would be happiest at a resort hotel.

20 Which of the following is an opinion expressed by the author in paragraph 8?

○ Nothing makes city-dwellers happier than a week in nature.

○ The best way to plan a vacation is to think about relaxing.

○ Swimming in a lake is the same as swimming in a pool.

○ Vacations are unnecessary if you live near a city park.

GO ON

3 Copyright © Pearson Education, Inc., or its affiliates. All Rights Reserved.

WRITTEN RESPONSE TO THE SELECTION

Look Back and Write Reread the pages 134–136. Think about all the different things that must happen to get food to the supermarket. Now write a list of directions explaining the process of getting fruits and vegetables from the farm to the store. Provide evidence to support your answer.

The information in the box below will help you remember what you should think about when you write your composition.

REMEMBER—YOU SHOULD

☐ write a list of directions to explain the process of how fruits and vegetables get from the farm to the store.

☐ write your directions clearly so that the reader understands the process.

☐ use time order words so that the reader can clearly follow the sequence of events.

☐ try to use correct spelling, capitalization, punctuation, grammar, and sentences.

3 Copyright © Pearson Education, Inc., or its affiliates. All Rights Reserved.

_____

_____

_____

_____

_____

_____

_____

_____

_____

_____

_____

_____

_____

_____

_____

_____

_____

_____

_____

3 Copyright © Pearson Education, Inc., or its affiliates. All Rights Reserved.

VOCABULARY

Directions

Find the word or words with the same meaning as the underlined word. Fill in the circle next to the answer.

1 Mom did some **errands**.

- ⭘ dishes
- ⭘ tasks
- ⭘ puzzles
- ⭘ races

2 Joe spoke **excitedly**.

- ⭘ eagerly
- ⭘ quietly
- ⭘ angrily
- ⭘ slowly

3 The tall vase **wobbled**.

- ⭘ broke
- ⭘ rocked
- ⭘ fell
- ⭘ leaked

4 Tara held the ladder **steady**.

- ⭘ close to her
- ⭘ gently
- ⭘ dangerously
- ⭘ still

5 Wilhelm carried the **bundles** to the car.

- ⭘ packages that are pretty
- ⭘ packages that are torn
- ⭘ packages that are heavy
- ⭘ packages that are tied

6 Nicole **arranged** the flowers.

- ⭘ hated
- ⭘ smelled
- ⭘ positioned
- ⭘ carried

7 He found the **unwrapped** package on the table.

- ⭘ sealed
- ⭘ tied up
- ⭘ opened
- ⭘ unopened

3 Copyright © Pearson Education, Inc., or its affiliates. All Rights Reserved.

GO ON

PHONICS

*D*irections

Find the word with the same vowel sound as the underlined word. Fill in the circle next to the answer.

8 The king's <u>crown</u> was made of gold.

Which word has the same sound as the <u>ow</u> in <u>crown</u>?

○ blow
○ crop
○ sound
○ swan

9 Each student took a turn to read <u>aloud</u>.

Which word has the same sound as the <u>ou</u> in <u>aloud</u>?

○ your
○ poor
○ shower
○ boat

10 This morning, her team hiked to the <u>tower</u>.

Which word has the same sound as <u>ow</u> in <u>tower</u>?

○ mow
○ our
○ morning
○ door

11 He thinks before he makes a <u>choice</u>.

Which word has the same sound as the <u>oi</u> in <u>choice</u>?

○ town
○ lion
○ you
○ royal

12 Larry stays <u>loyal</u> to his friends.

Which word has the same sound as the <u>oy</u> in <u>loyal</u>?

○ voice
○ vowel
○ loud
○ lower

COMPREHENSION

Smart Elephants

Elephants are one of the largest animals on land. Because they are so large, they have to eat a lot. They eat roots, grasses, fruit, and bark. They have big, flapping ears and long trunks.

At the circus, they can stand on a pedestal. At the zoo, they can spray water through their trunks like a fountain. But did you know that elephants can also paint pictures?

GO ON

3 Copyright © Pearson Education, Inc., or its affiliates. All Rights Reserved.

Elephants have very large brains. This makes them smart. They also have good memories. Elephants stay together in family groups. Parents teach the young elephants how to eat, use tools, and get along with other elephants. It is important to study how elephants interact because it helps us learn how their brains work.

Elephants are good at solving problems. Even though they have no hands, they can use tree branches as tools. Their trunk becomes like an arm and they hold the branch to scratch their backs or dig holes. Some elephants can even figure out how to unlock a cage and help the other elephants escape from the zoo! Other elephants can hold a paintbrush in their trunks and paint pictures.

Elephants have feelings. They help each other find food and care for their young. They go out of their way to avoid hurting each other. If one elephant gets hurt, the other elephants stay with him. If one elephant dies, the other elephants mourn. They hang their heads and are quiet. They are sad.

Elephants also enjoy playing. They splash in the water and make sounds like a trumpet. Some elephants can whistle and copy some sounds of human language.

Elephants can be seen in zoos and circuses. But they also live in the wild in Africa, India, and Asia. Some live in grassy areas. Others live in the rain forests. They live wherever they can find food and water. Sometimes they have to travel long distances to find food. Because of their smarts and social skills, elephants are able to survive difficult conditions.

Still, elephants are very special animals. Greater efforts should be made to protect them in the wild.

Directions

Choose the item that best answers each question about the selection you just read. Fill in the circle next to the answer.

3 Copyright © Pearson Education, Inc., or its affiliates. All Rights Reserved.

13 **Why do elephants have to eat so much?**

○ because they play so much
○ because they are so smart
○ because they have feelings
○ because they are so large

14 **Why does the author think it's important to study how elephants interact?**

○ to teach them how to do tricks
○ to learn how their brains work
○ to capture them for zoos
○ to know how they use tools

GO ON

15 In paragraph 4, the author describes how elephants escape zoos in order to

○ persuade readers to go to the circus.

○ tell why elephants should live in the wild.

○ give an example of how elephants solve problems.

○ describe how elephants copy human language.

16 Why does the author discuss elephants' feelings in paragraph 5?

○ to give information on how elephants relate to each other

○ to describe how elephants survive in the wild

○ to point out that elephants are often sad

○ to entertain the reader with stories of elephants playing

17 The selection discusses how elephants can copy the sounds of human language

○ to give details about how elephants have used tools.

○ before it discusses the size of their brains.

○ as a minor detail about how they are playful.

○ after it discusses where they live in the wild.

18 In paragraph 8, the author tries to persuade the reader that

○ elephants should be freed from zoos and circuses.

○ elephants should not be forced to paint pictures.

○ elephants should be kept in family groups.

○ elephants should be protected in the wild.

19 What is the author's purpose for writing the selection?

○ to inform the reader about elephant intelligence

○ to entertain the reader with lists of elephant tricks

○ to describe how elephants escape zoos

○ to persuade the reader to buy elephant paintings

20 Which detail supports the main idea that elephants are smart?

○ Elephants eat a lot of roots, grasses, fruit and bark.

○ Elephants are good at solving problems.

○ Elephants are found in Africa, India and Asia.

○ Elephants are one of the largest animals on land.

3 Copyright © Pearson Education, Inc., or its affiliates. All Rights Reserved.

GO ON

WRITTEN RESPONSE TO THE SELECTION

Look Back and Write Look back at page 180. Did Yeyo's kind words make Saruni happy? Use details from the selection to tell how he felt and why. Provide evidence to support your answer.

The information in the box below will help you remember what you should think about when you write your composition.

REMEMBER—YOU SHOULD

☐   explain if Yeyo's kind words make Saruni happy.

☐   make sure you support your answer with details from the story to tell how Saruni felt and why he felt that way.

☐   make sure that each sentence you write helps the reader understand your composition.

☐   try to use correct spelling, capitalization, punctuation, grammar, and sentences.

3 Copyright © Pearson Education, Inc., or its affiliates. All Rights Reserved.

3 Copyright © Pearson Education, Inc., or its affiliates. All Rights Reserved.

VOCABULARY

Directions

Find the word or words with the same meaning as the underlined word. Fill in the circle next to the answer.

1 The penguin waved its <u>flippers</u>.
- ○ organs for seeing
- ○ limbs for walking
- ○ limbs for swimming
- ○ wings for flying

2 My puppy <u>cuddles</u> with me.
- ○ curls up close
- ○ walks
- ○ goes to school
- ○ plays

3 Tina saw the tiny bird <u>hatch</u>.
- ○ eat seeds
- ○ come out of an egg
- ○ hide under a leaf
- ○ fly away

4 The lake was <u>frozen</u>.
- ○ iced over
- ○ full of fish
- ○ shallow
- ○ muddy

5 Tim's bird gently <u>pecks</u> with its beak.
- ○ digs
- ○ cleans
- ○ claws
- ○ strikes

6 Look how the kittens <u>snuggle</u> together!
- ○ run around
- ○ eat
- ○ get warm and cozy
- ○ chase mice

7 All birds <u>preen</u> their feathers.
- ○ chew
- ○ clean
- ○ admire
- ○ shed

3 Copyright © Pearson Education, Inc., or its affiliates. All Rights Reserved.

GO ON

WORD ANALYSIS

Directions

For each underlined word, choose the item that shows how to divide it correctly into syllables. Fill in the circle next to the answer.

8 The score is <u>even</u> at halftime.

- ○ eve | n
- ○ e | ven
- ○ even
- ○ ev | en

9 I would like some <u>lemon</u> in my water.

- ○ le | mon
- ○ l | emon
- ○ lem | on
- ○ lemo | n

10 The players will <u>divide</u> into teams.

- ○ d | ivide
- ○ divid | e
- ○ div | ide
- ○ di | vide

11 They <u>finish</u> the story with a surprise.

- ○ fini | sh
- ○ fin | ish
- ○ fi | nish
- ○ f | inish

12 Each <u>student</u> chooses a topic to research.

- ○ stu | dent
- ○ stud | ent
- ○ st | udent
- ○ stude | nt

COMPREHENSION

Ground Squirrels

Ground squirrels live across the world. They are cute and smart and can be a lot of fun to watch. But these furry animals are not for cuddling.

Young children may see these squirrels in parks or around their houses. They may want to pet or play with them because they think the squirrels are so adorable. But if children get too close, squirrels may become afraid and then bite. In these cases, ground squirrels can be harmful.

3 Copyright © Pearson Education, Inc., or its affiliates. All Rights Reserved.

GO ON

Ground squirrels look cute because they have large eyes. Their fur has mixed colors. It is light and dark gray with light brown and white flecks. Their tails are long but not very bushy.

Ground squirrels spend most of the day looking for food. They eat seeds, nuts, berries, grass, plants, roots, and sometimes bugs. They store some of their food. The squirrels dig small holes. Then they put the food in the hole. Finally, they cover the hole with dirt. They eat the stored food in winter when there is less food to find.

Ground squirrels have their babies in burrows in early spring. The babies stay under the ground for a couple of months. Then the young squirrels come out with their mothers. When they are young, they learn to stay near the holes and to look for food on the ground or in small bushes.

Some ground squirrels live in cold parts of the world. In winter, these squirrels go into a deep sleep until the weather becomes warmer. Then they wake up and come out of their holes. They start to look for food.

Some people may see ground squirrels and want to feed them. Many cities across the country warn that it is not safe to feed them. Even cities like Los Angeles put out warnings. They say, "Do not touch or feed the squirrels." When we learn about ground squirrels, we learn how to safely enjoy our furry friends.

Directions

Choose the item that best answers each question about the selection you just read. Fill in the circle next to the answer.

13 **Why does Los Angeles put out warnings about ground squirrels?**

○ to tell people about ground squirrel babies

○ to explain how to feed ground squirrels

○ to keep people safe from ground squirrels

○ to show people what ground squirrels look like

14 **What is the main idea of the passage?**

○ Ground squirrels may be cute, but do not feed or pet them.

○ Ground squirrels have large eyes, mixed gray fur, and long tails.

○ Ground squirrels dig small holes, put food in them, and cover them with dirt.

○ Ground squirrels that live in cold places go into a deep sleep.

3 Copyright © Pearson Education, Inc., or its affiliates. All Rights Reserved.

GO ON

15 How might ground squirrels be harmful to people?

○ Ground squirrels eat all of the grass and plants.

○ Ground squirrels may bite children.

○ Cities across the country put out warnings.

○ Ground squirrels are not harmful; they are for cuddling.

16 What happens to baby squirrels a couple of months after they are born?

○ They go into a deep sleep.

○ They come outside with their mothers.

○ They eat seeds and bugs.

○ They play with children.

17 Which detail is not found in the selection?

○ Ground squirrels are much larger than tree squirrels.

○ Baby ground squirrels stay underground for a couple of months.

○ Ground squirrels dig holes and store some of their food.

○ Ground squirrels have long tails.

18 How are ground squirrels probably different from tree squirrels?

○ Ground squirrels have much larger eyes.

○ Ground squirrels store some of their food.

○ Ground squirrels live under the ground.

○ Ground squirrels live in cold parts of the world.

19 If people do not feed ground squirrels, how do they survive?

○ They look for food on the ground or in small bushes.

○ They look for food in tall trees.

○ They go into a deep sleep.

○ They use their large eyes and long tails to find food.

20 Why do people want to touch ground squirrels?

○ because the ground squirrels eat interesting foods

○ because people need more pets

○ because the ground squirrels are furry and adorable

○ because the ground squirrels are sleeping

GO ON

3 Copyright © Pearson Education, Inc., or its affiliates. All Rights Reserved.

WRITTEN RESPONSE TO THE SELECTION

> **Look Back and Write** Look back at the question on page 208. Find information in the text about how penguins protect their chicks against the extreme cold weather. Write a response to the question.

The information in the box below will help you remember what you should think about when you write your composition.

REMEMBER—YOU SHOULD

☐   explain how penguins protect their chicks against the extreme cold weather.

☐   make sure each sentence you write serves the purpose for which you are writing.

☐   make sure you use details from the text to support your answer.

☐   try to use correct spelling, capitalization, punctuation, grammar, and sentences.

---

3 Copyright © Pearson Education, Inc., or its affiliates. All Rights Reserved.

3 Copyright © Pearson Education, Inc., or its affiliates. All Rights Reserved.

VOCABULARY

Directions

Find the word or words with the same meaning as the underlined word. Fill in the circle next to the correct answer.

1 Omar put his <u>trophies</u> on the top shelf.

○ favorite clothes
○ prizes for victory
○ valuable books
○ sports equipment

2 Everyone said the new puppy was <u>adorable</u>.

○ very cute
○ very tiny
○ very soft
○ very sick

3 The <u>mention</u> of the beach got Liz excited.

○ sight
○ plan
○ chance
○ talk

4 Reggie found an <u>iguana</u> sunning itself by the poolside.

○ a dangerous snake
○ a large lizard
○ a spotted frog
○ a tiny turtle

5 When driving in a new town, it is important to follow directions <u>exactly</u>.

○ partly
○ one at a time
○ slightly
○ precisely

6 John was <u>compassionate</u> when Angela caught the flu.

○ disappointed
○ troubled
○ understanding
○ annoyed

7 Mr. Trigg said the tree in his backyard was <u>mature</u>.

○ fully grown
○ needing water
○ just planted
○ unwanted

3 Copyright © Pearson Education, Inc., or its affiliates. All Rights Reserved.

GO ON

WORD ANALYSIS

*D*irections

For each underlined word, choose the item that shows how to divide it correctly into syllables. Fill in the circle next to the answer.

8 He put the soup on the <u>table</u>.

- ○ ta | ble
- ○ t | able
- ○ tab | le
- ○ tabl | e

9 The team made a <u>circle</u>.

- ○ circ | le
- ○ cir | cle
- ○ ci | rcle
- ○ circl | e

10 The <u>eagle</u> flies over the nest.

- ○ eagl | e
- ○ eag | le
- ○ e | agle
- ○ ea | gle

11 He listened for the <u>whistle</u> before running.

- ○ whi | stle
- ○ whis | tle
- ○ whist | le
- ○ wh | istle

12 She baked a <u>simple</u> apple pie.

- ○ si | mple
- ○ simp | le
- ○ s | imple
- ○ sim | ple

COMPREHENSION

Missing Dinner

Jen was sitting on the living room sofa. She was reading a mystery book. The dog, Teddy, was lying at her feet. The cat, Zoey, was sleeping in her lap. She could hear her mom in the kitchen, clattering plates and taking out supplies for dinner.

"What are we having, Mom?" Jen called.

"Fish," Mom replied. Jen groaned. She didn't like fish.

Mom came to the door. "Don't complain, Jen. Fish is good for you. I'm just going to leave it on the table for a minute and go check the laundry." The dog, Teddy, got up and followed her mom out of the room.

When Jen sighed, Zoey jumped off her lap. Jen turned back to her book.

GO ON

3 Copyright © Pearson Education, Inc., or its affiliates. All Rights Reserved.

Ten minutes later Jen's mom was at the door again, an angry look on her face. "I don't think this is funny, Jen. What did you do with the fish?"

Jen looked up, surprised. "Nothing," she said. "I didn't touch the fish."

"Well, someone did," Jen's mom said.

They both went into the kitchen. Sure enough, there was an empty plate on the table. Both Teddy, the dog, and Zoey, the cat, were sitting on the kitchen floor, their eyes wide with innocence.

"It had to be one of the animals," Jen's mom said. "But which one?"

"It's a mystery," Jen said. "But I think I can solve it."

"Let's hear it," Jen's mom said with a smile.

"Well," Jen said, "Both Teddy and Zoey like fish, so both of them would follow the smell." Jen went over to the empty plate. "There's a little piece of dark fur here near the plate, but both Teddy and Zoey have dark fur. Let's look for prints. Teddy has a longer paw and Zoey has a rounder paw."

Jen's mom came up and looked with her. But there were no prints on the table.

"I know!" Jen cried. "Teddy is a small dog. He can't jump very high. Only Zoey the cat could have jumped up to the table and stolen the fish."

"You'll make a great detective," Jen's mom came up and hugged her. "Now can you solve the mystery of what we're going to eat for dinner tonight?"

"That's an easy one," Jen said. "Anything but fish!"

Directions
Choose the item that best answers each question about the selection you just read. Fill in the circle next to the answer.

13 In paragraph 1, what is a comparison between Teddy and Zoey?
- ○ They are both sleeping in Jen's lap.
- ○ They are both in the living room with Jen.
- ○ They are both in the kitchen with Jen's mom.
- ○ They are both lying at Jen's feet.

14 Which of the following events happens first?
- ○ Jen's mom goes to check the laundry.
- ○ Jen solves the mystery of the missing fish.
- ○ Jen's mom puts the plate of fish on the table.
- ○ Teddy and Zoey are sitting on the kitchen floor.

GO ON

3 Copyright © Pearson Education, Inc., or its affiliates. All Rights Reserved.

15 In paragraph 6, what causes Jen's mom to think that Jen took the fish?

○ Jen offered to help cook.

○ Jen complained about dinner.

○ Jen never got up from the sofa.

○ Jen often fed her dinner to the dog.

16 What is a contrast between Jen and her mom?

○ Jen likes to cook; her mom likes to read mysteries.

○ Jen takes care of Teddy; her mom takes care of Zoey.

○ Jen doesn't like fish; her mom likes fish.

○ Jen does her homework while her mom does laundry.

17 In paragraph 13, what is a comparison between Teddy and Zoey?

○ Both have round paws.

○ Both have dark fur.

○ Both dislike fish.

○ Both have long paws.

18 In paragraph 13, what is a contrast between Teddy and Zoey?

○ Teddy has light fur; Zoey has dark fur.

○ Teddy likes fish; Zoey doesn't like fish.

○ Teddy is on the floor; Zoey is on the table.

○ Teddy has a longer paw; Zoey has a rounder paw.

19 In paragraph 15, what contrast between Teddy and Zoey helps Jen solve the mystery?

○ Only Zoey can jump to the table.

○ Only Teddy likes fish.

○ Only Zoey has dark fur.

○ Only Teddy can jump to the table.

20 By the end of the story, Jen's mom is

○ mad at Zoey for jumping on the table.

○ happy that they don't have to eat fish.

○ proud of Jen for solving the mystery.

○ angry that there is nothing to eat.

3 Copyright © Pearson Education, Inc., or its affiliates. All Rights Reserved.

WRITTEN RESPONSE TO THE SELECTION

Look Back and Write Look back at page 250. Alex's mother is concerned that he is not ready to have a pet. Do you think this is true? Provide details as evidence to support your answer.

The information in the box below will help you remember what you should think about when you write your composition.

REMEMBER—YOU SHOULD

☐ explain if you think it is true that Alex is not ready to have a pet.

☐ make sure you include details about Alex to support your answer.

☐ make sure each sentence you write helps the reader understand your composition.

☐ try to use correct spelling, capitalization, punctuation, grammar, and sentences.

3 Copyright © Pearson Education, Inc., or its affiliates. All Rights Reserved.

GO ON

_____

_____

_____

_____

_____

_____

_____

_____

_____

_____

_____

_____

_____

_____

_____

_____

_____

_____

_____

_____

_____

_____

3 Copyright © Pearson Education, Inc., or its affiliates. All Rights Reserved.

VOCABULARY

Directions

Find the word or words with the same meaning as the underlined word. Fill in the circle next to the answer.

1 The bag began to <u>strain</u> because it was full.

○ sit
○ balance
○ practice
○ stretch

2 An <u>enormous</u> cloud blocked the sun.

○ fluffy
○ dark
○ low
○ huge

3 Ella <u>scattered</u> seeds in the garden.

○ watered
○ sprinkled
○ covered
○ gathered

4 I bent down to fix my <u>shoelaces</u>.

○ tongue of a shoe
○ top of a sock
○ cords for tying shoes
○ tread on a shoe

5 Sasha showed us his stamp <u>collection</u>.

○ bin of papers
○ set of objects
○ pile of trash
○ box of toys

6 The <u>butterflies</u> were all so colorful.

○ insects
○ birds
○ kites
○ papers

3 Copyright © Pearson Education, Inc., or its affiliates. All Rights Reserved.

GO ON

WORD ANALYSIS

Directions
Find the compound word in each sentence. Fill in the circle next to the answer.

7 I walked along the empty railroad.
- ○ railroad
- ○ walked
- ○ along
- ○ empty

8 Have you seen my sister's missing earring?
- ○ sister's
- ○ seen
- ○ earring
- ○ missing

9 Our class made popcorn in a machine.
- ○ machine
- ○ popcorn
- ○ our
- ○ class

10 A snowstorm is going to come later this week.
- ○ going
- ○ later
- ○ week
- ○ snowstorm

11 Don't put too much wood in the fireplace.
- ○ don't
- ○ fireplace
- ○ much
- ○ wood

12 Our teacher's birthday is coming up next month.
- ○ teacher's
- ○ coming
- ○ birthday
- ○ month

COMPREHENSION

The Robin: A Sign of Spring

In many places, the coming of robins signals the beginning of spring. During the winter, robins live in large groups. But early in spring, they leave their groups to look for mates.

These birds are easy to spot, with their dark heads and bright red chests. The colors on a female are a little lighter than on a male robin. They are also easy to spot because robins live around people.

3   Copyright © Pearson Education, Inc., or its affiliates. All Rights Reserved.

Often robins can be found on a lawn looking for worms and insects. Robins do not like to eat seeds. That's why they don't bother to go to bird feeders. In winter they eat berries.

Because robins arrive at their breeding grounds so early in the spring, many trees don't have leaves yet. But evergreen trees keep their needles or leaves all year. So many robins build their nests in evergreens for protection. Robins also build nests on buildings and fences.

Robins make their nests out of twigs, grass, and mud. The female builds the nest, but the male helps by bringing the building supplies to the tree.

The female shapes the nest by getting inside and pushing against it. Sometimes a robin will have a line of mud across its chest. That means she's been building a nest.

Each day the female lays one blue egg until there are three or four. Once the eggs hatch, the babies must be fed. Both parents do this job. The young birds don't look exactly like their parents yet because their breasts are spotted. When the young birds leave the nest, the male takes over feeding them by himself. That's when the female starts a second family.

When winter is on its way, the robins will return to their large groups. But they'll be back soon enough to signal the start of the next spring!

Directions
Choose the item that best answers each question about the selection you just read. Fill in the circle next to the answer.

3 Copyright © Pearson Education, Inc., or its affiliates. All Rights Reserved.

13 In paragraph 1, what detail lets you conclude that robins are not visible to people during the winter?

○ In the winter, robins live in large groups.

○ The coming of robins signals springtime.

○ Robins leave their groups in early spring.

○ In large groups, robins are easy to spot.

14 What conclusion can you draw from paragraph 2?

○ Robins live around people in order to find food.

○ Bright red chests make robins victims of hunters.

○ Robins are the most recognizable bird.

○ It is possible to tell males and females apart.

GO ON

15 Which detail helps you conclude that robins are not afraid of people?

○ They build nests on buildings and fences.

○ They do not like to eat seeds.

○ They make nests of twigs, grass, and mud.

○ They don't bother to go to bird feeders.

16 What is one effect of robins arriving at breeding grounds in early spring?

○ They use their bodies to shape the nest.

○ They use evergreens for protection.

○ They find worms and insects on lawns.

○ They have lines of mud across their chests.

17 What conclusion can you draw about how robins build nests?

○ Robins don't worry about safety when choosing a spot for their nests.

○ The male robin has the harder job to build the nest.

○ The female robin has the harder job to build the nest.

○ Both male and female have important roles in building the nest.

18 What detail supports the main idea that robins are easy to spot?

○ They have loud mating songs.

○ They have bright red chests.

○ They appear in large flocks.

○ They keep busy looking for worms and insects.

19 Compared to the adult robins, the young robins

○ do not join groups in winter.

○ are a little redder than their parents.

○ have spotted breasts.

○ are experts at finding food.

20 What conclusion can you draw from paragraphs 7 and 8?

○ Female robins spend most of their time feeding the young.

○ Young robins leave the nest in summertime.

○ Robins follow the same pattern every year.

○ Young robins are difficult to take care of.

3 Copyright © Pearson Education, Inc., or its affiliates. All Rights Reserved.

GO ON

WRITTEN RESPONSE TO THE SELECTION

> **Look Back and Write** What made Prudy realize that she had a problem? Look at pages 284–286 to find out. Write about her creative solution. Use details from the story in your answer.

The information in the box below will help you remember what you should think about when you write your composition.

REMEMBER—YOU SHOULD

☐   make sure you first understand and explain what Prudy's problem is.

☐   explain Prudy's creative solution to her problem.

☐   write about Prudy's creative solution to her problem in detail so that the reader knows what you are saying.

☐   try to use correct spelling, capitalization, punctuation, grammar, and sentences.

3 Copyright © Pearson Education, Inc., or its affiliates. All Rights Reserved.

GO ON

_____

_____

_____

_____

_____

_____

_____

_____

_____

_____

_____

_____

_____

_____

_____

_____

_____

_____

_____

3 Copyright © Pearson Education, Inc., or its affiliates. All Rights Reserved.

VOCABULARY

Directions

Find the word or words with the same meaning as the underlined word. Fill in the circle next to the answer.

1 The man is <u>lazy</u>.
- ○ not driving very quickly
- ○ not very friendly
- ○ not working hard
- ○ not remembering things

2 It is time to gather the <u>crops</u>.
- ○ garden tools
- ○ children
- ○ animals
- ○ plants grown for food

3 Mr. Sanchez and Dad are <u>partners</u> in the work.
- ○ people who are best friends
- ○ people who work as a team
- ○ people who grew up together
- ○ people who rescue others

4 That girl <u>cheated</u> me.
- ○ called
- ○ helped
- ○ tricked
- ○ watched

5 Nick told us his <u>clever</u> idea.
- ○ odd
- ○ smart
- ○ new
- ○ silly

6 The United States is a country of great <u>wealth</u>.
- ○ riches
- ○ homes
- ○ people
- ○ schools

7 I painted the <u>bottom</u> of the box.
- ○ inside
- ○ lower part
- ○ outside
- ○ top part

3 Copyright © Pearson Education, Inc., or its affiliates. All Rights Reserved.

GO ON

PHONICS

*D*irections

Find the word or words that best answer each question. Fill in the circle next to the answer.

8 Throw the ball to me.

Which word has the same sound as the thr in throw?

○ those
○ troll
○ thread
○ tread

9 Don't splash water in the tub.

Which word has the same sound as the spl in splash?

○ spray
○ pals
○ spin
○ splurge

10 I can't wait for spring to come.

Which word has the same sound as the spr in spring?

○ spread
○ spine
○ singer
○ strip

11 I like the striped shirt.

Which word has the same sound as the str in striped?

○ poster
○ style
○ street
○ speak

12 Did you hear that loud scream?

Which word has the same sound as the scr in scream?

○ scare
○ screech
○ store
○ skate

3 Copyright © Pearson Education, Inc., or its affiliates. All Rights Reserved.

GO ON

COMPREHENSION

The Money Game

Professional athletes make a lot of money. The more popular they are, the more money they make. Some football, baseball, and basketball players make millions of dollars a year. Just for playing a game! Compared to that, doctors and teachers make very little.

What does this say about our way of life? How can we explain the high pay of professional athletes? Is paying players so much wrong? Or does it make sense?

Many people say that paying players so much money hurts the game. In some cases, players make a lot of money because they are famous rather than because they play well. Also, athletes who join a team straight out of high school often get damaged by the money. These players are rich before they have time to grow up as a player—or as a person.

Worse, young people look to athletes as role models. These young people see their heroes make a lot of money for playing a game. Then they put their hopes for the future into sports rather than school.

At the same time, there are good reasons that players make so much. For one thing, popular players make huge amounts of money for the team. Popular players sell tickets, TV ads, T-shirts, sports jerseys, signed balls, and other souvenirs. Sports teams work like any other business. Teams pay their employees based on how much money they bring in for the company.

Also, professional athletes are very rare. These players work their entire lives to reach the professional level. They are at the top of their game. There are so few others who play that well that they are paid fairly for their talents.

Finally, professional ballplayers are entertainers, just like movie stars. People love to watch exciting ballgames. Ballplayers give pleasure to millions of fans. If movie stars make a lot of money, so should sports stars.

Sports stars have a shorter career than movie stars. Often these players hurt their bodies playing at such a high level. Many end their careers early, their bodies broken. They are paid fairly for giving their entire lives to the game.

3 Copyright © Pearson Education, Inc., or its affiliates. All Rights Reserved.

GO ON

COMPREHENSION

Directions

Choose the item that best answers each question about the selection you just read. Fill in the circle next to the answer.

13 Based on paragraph 2, the author wrote the selection in order to question

- ⃝ the price of sports tickets.
- ⃝ the pay of professional athletes.
- ⃝ the talent of professional athletes.
- ⃝ the pay of doctors and teachers.

14 What is the author's purpose in paragraph 3?

- ⃝ to explain how high pay hurts the game
- ⃝ to describe how rich young players are
- ⃝ to show that talented athletes are rare
- ⃝ to argue that athletes are poor losers

15 In paragraph 4, the author is trying to

- ⃝ describe why young people want to be rich.
- ⃝ argue that athletes shouldn't be role models.
- ⃝ praise athletes who are good role models.
- ⃝ tell young people to join sports teams in high school.

16 Which fact in paragraph 6 supports the conclusion that professional athletes are paid fairly?

- ⃝ They are as good at business as they are at playing sports.
- ⃝ There are very few athletes who play as well.
- ⃝ They have so much talent, they never have to practice.
- ⃝ There are many other players who are just as good.

17 Why does the author compare sports teams to businesses?

- ⃝ to complain about how expensive sports tickets have gotten
- ⃝ to show that talent has nothing to do with business
- ⃝ to explain that athletes are paid for the money they bring in
- ⃝ to describe the different items that sports teams sell to fans

18 The information in paragraph 6 lets you generalize that

- ⃝ very few people are talented enough to become professional athletes.
- ⃝ professional athletes make most of their money from TV advertisements.
- ⃝ very few people work as hard as professional athletes.
- ⃝ all it takes to become a professional athlete is hard work.

19 In paragraph 7, what two things does the author compare?

- ⃝ movie stars and sports fans
- ⃝ sports stars and movie stars
- ⃝ sports fans and sports stars
- ⃝ role models and sports stars

20 In paragraph 8, the author tries to persuade readers that

- ⃝ professional players have long careers.
- ⃝ professional players never grow up.
- ⃝ professional players are always healthy.
- ⃝ professional players are paid fairly.

GO ON

3 Copyright © Pearson Education, Inc., or its affiliates. All Rights Reserved.

WRITTEN RESPONSE TO THE SELECTION

Look Back and Write Look back at page 320. Why does Bear think he has been cheated again? Provide evidence to support your answer.

The information in the box below will help you remember what you should think about when you write your composition.

REMEMBER—YOU SHOULD

☐ explain why Bear thinks he has been cheated again.

☐ use details about the kind of crops Hare planted to support your answer.

☐ organize your ideas as you write to help the reader understand your composition.

☐ try to use correct spelling, capitalization, punctuation, grammar, and sentences.

3 Copyright © Pearson Education, Inc., or its affiliates. All Rights Reserved.

3 Copyright © Pearson Education, Inc., or its affiliates. All Rights Reserved.

VOCABULARY

Directions
Find the word or words with the same meaning as the underlined word. Fill in the circle next to the answer.

1 The bird's <u>bill</u> was yellow and flat.
- ○ wing
- ○ foot
- ○ back
- ○ beak

2 Lauren stood on the station <u>platform</u>.
- ○ raised floor
- ○ flat step
- ○ slanted roof
- ○ boat deck

3 The <u>hunters</u> went outside.
- ○ students who leave class early
- ○ people who kill wild animals
- ○ people who study pine trees
- ○ animals that eat flowering plants

4 This <u>material</u> is very soft.
- ○ substance used to make something
- ○ the outer part of a jacket
- ○ a large blanket
- ○ the fur of an animal

5 This car is a <u>ton</u>.
- ○ a brand of truck
- ○ a color like brown
- ○ a unit of weight
- ○ an age over five years

6 James broke the <u>twigs</u>.
- ○ glass cups
- ○ long pencils
- ○ plastic toys
- ○ small branches

7 There was a trail of snail <u>goo</u> in the garden.
- ○ something sharp
- ○ something dry
- ○ something hot
- ○ something sticky

3 Copyright © Pearson Education, Inc., or its affiliates. All Rights Reserved.

GO ON

PHONICS

Directions

Find the word that best answers each question. Fill in the circle next to the answer.

8 Heather's <u>father</u> likes to cook.

Which word has the same sound as the th in <u>father</u>?

- ○ feather
- ○ fatter
- ○ feeder
- ○ faded

9 The <u>telephone</u> is ringing.

Which word has the same sound as the <u>ph</u> in <u>telephone</u>?

- ○ pants
- ○ leap
- ○ farm
- ○ stone

10 Ted is <u>washing</u> the dishes.

Which word has the same sound as the <u>ng</u> in <u>washing</u>?

- ○ wish
- ○ string
- ○ sign
- ○ again

11 The <u>machine</u> makes buttons from plastic.

Which word has the same sound as the <u>ch</u> in <u>machine</u>?

- ○ meaning
- ○ wasted
- ○ matching
- ○ fashion

12 I lost my <u>shoe</u> playing soccer.

Which word has the same sound as the <u>sh</u> in <u>shoe</u>?

- ○ sorry
- ○ chance
- ○ fish
- ○ scooter

COMPREHENSION

Why We Dream

Doctor Margaret Chang studies how people sleep. She wants to know why we dream. Understanding sleep helps us learn more about the brain.

Dr. Chang works in a lab. Many patients come to the lab so that Dr. Chang can watch them sleep. She asks each patient to lie down on a bed. Then Dr. Chang connects him or her to a machine with a screen. It is hard for some patients to fall asleep, but eventually they do.

3 Copyright © Pearson Education, Inc., or its affiliates. All Rights Reserved.

The machine with the screen is central to Dr. Chang's work. Dr. Chang has learned that when a patient first falls asleep, the screen does not show very much. But then different lights come on. The machine uses colors to keep track of which parts of the brain are active while a person is sleeping. It looks like fireworks on the screen. Dr. Chang prints out pictures from the machine to study.

Dr. Chang has learned that everyone goes through cycles when he or she sleeps. In one cycle, called Light Sleep, the heart rate slows and body temperature decreases. During another cycle, our eyes move quickly back and forth even though our eyes stay closed. Most dreams happen during this cycle.

Dr. Chang asks people what they dream about, but often they don't remember anything. They think they did not have any dreams. But we have many dreams, even if we don't remember them in the morning. Dr. Chang knows that people dream because she has pictures from the machine. The pictures show yellow, orange, and red spots covering different sections of the brain.

All of the colors in the picture mean something. The yellow part covers the visual area of the brain. This means the person was seeing something as he or she slept. The red part covers the section of the brain that experiences fear. People with red in their pictures were afraid of something in their dreams.

Dr. Chang hopes to learn more about what happens when we dream. As she compares different pictures, she comes to understand which parts of the brain are most active. She also learns when in the sleep cycles this activity occurs.

Directions

Choose the item that best answers each question about the selection you just read. Fill in the circle next to the answer.

13 What detail supports the main idea that the machine is important to Dr. Chang's studies?

- ○ We have many dreams, even if we don't remember them.
- ○ When dreaming, our eyes are closed while moving back and forth.
- ○ The machine keeps track of brain activity during sleep.
- ○ Dr. Chang hopes to learn more about dreaming.

14 What is the topic of this selection?

- ○ why people have nightmares
- ○ the first sleep cycle
- ○ colorful dreams
- ○ brain activity during sleep

GO ON

3 Copyright © Pearson Education, Inc., or its affiliates. All Rights Reserved.

15 **What is the main idea of paragraph 4?**

○ Everyone goes through sleep cycles.

○ The eyes move back and forth during dreaming.

○ The heart rate slows during Light Sleep.

○ Dr. Change prints out pictures from the machine.

16 **Dr. Change studies how people sleep because**

○ she wants to know how long people sleep.

○ she wants to learn more about the brain.

○ she wants to hear the stories of dreams.

○ she wants to study human memory.

17 **In Dr. Chang's lab, what step comes after she connects a patient to the machine?**

○ She asks them to lie down on a bed.

○ Eventually they fall asleep.

○ The screen does not show very much.

○ She prints out pictures from the machine.

18 **Which detail supports the main idea that all the colors in Dr. Chang's pictures mean something?**

○ The pictures show yellow, orange, and red spots.

○ The machine's pictures prove that people dream.

○ The brain is active while people are sleeping.

○ The red part covers the section that experiences fear.

19 **What conclusion can you draw from paragraph 6?**

○ The brain is all the same.

○ Different parts of the brain do different things.

○ The brain doesn't think anything during sleep.

○ Parts of the brain act differently when we're awake.

20 **Which detail supports the main idea that Dr. Chang will learn more about dreams?**

○ There's a lot about the brain that we don't know about.

○ Yellow in the picture means the sleeping people were seeing something.

○ Comparing pictures, Dr. Chang learns the most active parts of the brain.

○ Her patients often don't remember anything about their dreams.

3 Copyright © Pearson Education, Inc., or its affiliates. All Rights Reserved.

WRITTEN RESPONSE TO THE SELECTION

Look Back and Write Look back at the amazing bird nests. Choose one that you find interesting. Write a paragraph telling what makes that nest amazing. Be sure to include facts and details from the article to support your answer.

The information in the box below will help you remember what you should think about when you write your composition.

REMEMBER—YOU SHOULD

☐ explain why the nest you chose is amazing.

☐ make sure you support your ideas with facts and details from the article.

☐ make sure you use descriptive words about the bird nest to help the reader understand what makes the nest amazing.

☐ try to use correct spelling, capitalization, punctuation, grammar, and sentences.

3 Copyright © Pearson Education, Inc., or its affiliates. All Rights Reserved.

_____

_____

_____

_____

_____

_____

_____

_____

_____

_____

_____

_____

_____

_____

_____

_____

_____

_____

_____

_____

_____

_____

_____

_____

_____

3 Copyright © Pearson Education, Inc., or its affiliates. All Rights Reserved.

VOCABULARY

Directions
Find the word or words with the same meaning as the underlined word. Fill in the circle next to the answer.

1 Tracy drank a soda with <u>artificial</u> sugar.
- ○ unnatural
- ○ extra
- ○ flavored
- ○ strong

2 The bakery put a <u>raisin</u> on top of each cupcake.
- ○ fresh cherry
- ○ chocolate chip
- ○ jellybean
- ○ dried grape

3 By next year this <u>area</u> will be a playground.
- ○ construction site
- ○ large garden
- ○ particular space
- ○ useless land

4 Miles wanted <u>proof</u> that he had lost the race.
- ○ evidence to determine truth
- ○ corrected math problems
- ○ opinions of people present
- ○ papers to add results

5 This summer we decided to <u>raise</u> tomatoes.
- ○ pick
- ○ grow
- ○ sell
- ○ cut

6 Allison mixed in a <u>preservative</u> before boiling the fruit.
- ○ ingredient that makes food easier to freeze
- ○ powder that makes food taste better
- ○ mixer that keeps food from getting hard
- ○ additive that keeps food fresh

7 The <u>grapevine</u> does best in full sun.
- ○ necklace made of grape-shaped beads
- ○ small bush for growing raisins
- ○ climbing plant on which grapes grow
- ○ wooden support for purple flowers

3 Copyright © Pearson Education, Inc., or its affiliates. All Rights Reserved.

WORD ANALYSIS

Directions

Find the word or words with the same meaning as the underlined word. Fill in the circle next to the answer.

8 She <u>couldn't</u> open the door.

- ○ cannot
- ○ should not
- ○ could not
- ○ were not

9 I <u>won't</u> go to the store today.

- ○ will not
- ○ would not
- ○ could not
- ○ want to

10 I <u>didn't</u> hear what you said.

- ○ did
- ○ did not
- ○ cannot
- ○ do

11 You <u>can't</u> play that.

- ○ could not
- ○ should not
- ○ like to
- ○ cannot

12 We <u>weren't</u> at the game.

- ○ were
- ○ were not
- ○ played
- ○ won

COMPREHENSION

Antarctica

When we think of southern places, we think of warm places. But Antarctica is the most southern land mass. It is also the coldest place on Earth. In the winter, it can get as cold as 90°C below freezing. It is so dry and windy that some people call it a frozen desert. Most of the land is covered in ice. Some of the ice is a mile thick.

No country owns Antarctica. It has no money, no farms, and no people. Though some countries say they want land there, the Antarctic Treaty says that the land is only for research in science. No country can have military or test weapons there. Taking resources from the land is illegal.

GO ON

3 Copyright © Pearson Education, Inc., or its affiliates. All Rights Reserved.

The only people who can stay on Antarctica are scientists. Most scientists stay for no more than six months. These scientists come from many different countries and study many different things. Some study the wildlife—the penguins, the whales, and the seals. Others study geography—the mountains, the volcanoes, and the more than 70 lakes under the ice. Others study the weather.

Visiting scientists have to watch out for the cold. Believe it or not, they also have to beware of the sun. Because the snow reflects almost all of the ultraviolet light from the sun, scientists on the ice have to wear powerful sunscreen.

Many scientists feel lucky for the chance to study such an interesting place. They also see the importance of protecting Antarctica for science.

There are many special things to see in the atmosphere of Antarctica. Because of its position in relation to the sun, there are 24 hours of sunlight during the summer and 24 hours of darkness during the winter. *Diamond dust* is made of low clouds of ice crystals. It is also possible to see *sun dogs*, or bright spots of light near the sun. At night there is a glow in the sky caused by *solar winds*, which is plasma given off by the sun.

Because it has no light pollution, Antarctica is the best place on Earth from which to see the stars.

Directions
Choose the item that best answers each question about the selection you just read. Fill in the circle next to the answer.

13 **What conclusion can you draw from paragraph 1?**

○ Antarctica is a popular place to visit.

○ There is nothing to study about Antarctica.

○ Antarctica is full of natural resources.

○ It is difficult to survive on Antarctica.

14 **The fact that Antarctica is called a "frozen desert" lets you draw what conclusion?**

○ There is very little rainfall.

○ Antarctica is full of cactuses.

○ Antarctica has many mountains.

○ Desert animals live there.

GO ON

3 Copyright © Pearson Education, Inc., or its affiliates. All Rights Reserved.

15 What conclusion can you draw from paragraph 3?

○ Wildlife in Antarctica is more interesting than its geography.

○ Many different types of scientists are interested in Antarctica.

○ Scientists race to study Antarctica before it disappears.

○ Weather in Antarctica is constantly changing.

16 What conclusion can you draw about the scientific studies done on Antarctica?

○ They are only done in the summer months.

○ They can't be done anywhere else on Earth.

○ The cold gets in the way of science.

○ The experiments cost millions of dollars.

17 In this selection, the author is trying to persuade readers that Antarctica

○ should be preserved for science.

○ should be opened to tourists.

○ should be left alone.

○ should be given to a nearby country.

18 Which of the following details supports the main idea that there are interesting things to see in Antarctica's atmosphere?

○ Visitors have to be careful of ultraviolet light.

○ Many scientists feel lucky to study there.

○ Diamond dust is made of low clouds of ice crystals.

○ There are more than 70 lakes below the ice.

19 The terms in paragraph 6 are italicized in order to

○ point out words that are hard to read.

○ point out words that are defined in the paragraph.

○ remind the teacher to write them on the board.

○ tell the reader to skip over the words.

20 What conclusion can you draw from the selection?

○ There are no scientists studying in Antarctica during the winter.

○ Diamond dust and sun dogs can be seen at other places on Earth.

○ Spending longer than six months in Antarctica makes you sick.

○ Some of the scientists in Antarctica are studying outer space.

3 Copyright © Pearson Education, Inc., or its affiliates. All Rights Reserved.

GO ON

WRITTEN RESPONSE TO THE SELECTION

> **Look Back and Write** There is nothing wasted with raisins. Look back at page 392. Tell how raisins are used. Provide evidence to support your answer.

The information in the box below will help you remember what you should think about when you write your composition.

REMEMBER—YOU SHOULD

☐ tell how raisins are used.

☐ write about the different ways raisins are used in detail so that the reader really understands what you are saying.

☐ make sure you support your ideas with evidence from the text.

☐ try to use correct spelling, capitalization, punctuation, grammar, and sentences.

Copyright © Pearson Education, Inc., or its affiliates. All Rights Reserved. 3

GO ON

3 Copyright © Pearson Education, Inc., or its affiliates. All Rights Reserved.

Name _____

VOCABULARY

Directions

Find the word or words with the same meaning as the underlined word. Fill in the circle next to the answer.

1 The deer's <u>antlers</u> looked sharp.
○ ears
○ legs
○ cheeks
○ horns

2 Jessie <u>imagined</u> the story.
○ wrote
○ listened to
○ copied
○ made up

3 Her book was printed in different <u>languages</u>.
○ colors of ink
○ types of speech
○ sizes of print
○ kinds of covers

4 Rebecca was the <u>narrator</u>.
○ teacher
○ author
○ speaker
○ builder

5 A hawk flew <u>overhead</u>.
○ nearby
○ above
○ down
○ around

6 Tom <u>poked</u> a hole through the page.
○ pushed with a finger
○ shook violently
○ pulled away a piece of
○ slapped the back of

3 Copyright © Pearson Education, Inc., or its affiliates. All Rights Reserved.

GO ON

WORD ANALYSIS

Directions
Find the prefix in the underlined word. Fill in the circle next to the answer.

7 My dog always <u>disobeys</u> me.

- ◯ dis
- ◯ obey
- ◯ eys
- ◯ s

8 The folders are <u>mislabeled</u>.

- ◯ labeled
- ◯ label
- ◯ ed
- ◯ mis

9 Julie was <u>uninterested</u> in the movie.

- ◯ interest
- ◯ un
- ◯ ed
- ◯ in

10 I'm going to <u>redo</u> the project.

- ◯ do
- ◯ red
- ◯ re
- ◯ redo

11 It is <u>dishonest</u> to tell a lie.

- ◯ dish
- ◯ dis
- ◯ honest
- ◯ est

12 Try not to <u>misspell</u> any words on the poster.

- ◯ mis
- ◯ miss
- ◯ spell
- ◯ pell

GO ON

3 Copyright © Pearson Education, Inc., or its affiliates. All Rights Reserved.

COMPREHENSION

The Tree House

Setting: A tree house at night.

LINDSAY: What was that noise?

JEN: What are you babbling about? Toss me that blanket. I'm freezing.

(Rustling in the backyard.)

LINDSAY: I'm positive I heard something. Didn't you? What if somebody's out there?

JEN: You're definitely imagining things. Stop worrying and let's have fun! It's so cool that we get to have a sleepover in your tree house.

LINDSAY: I don't know. It's awfully dark outside. Maybe we should go inside and watch TV instead.

JEN: We can't go in now! It's not even that late yet. Let's tell ghost stories. That will get you really terrified!

LINDSAY: That's not funny. *(A loud bump shakes the tree house.)* Shhhh. What was that? Someone's out there, I'm sure of it. Jen, I'm so scared. What are we going to do? *(LINDSAY inches toward the back of the tree house, hiding under a blanket. The top of a head appears in the entryway.)*

LINDSAY *(angrily):* David! Why are you wandering around in the dark?

JEN *(laughing):* Relax. It's just your brother. I told you not to worry! Now there are more of us to tell scary stories. Unless, of course, you're too afraid. . . .

LINDSAY: Me? Afraid? I knew it was David all along. I just wanted to see if I could scare you!

3 Copyright © Pearson Education, Inc., or its affiliates. All Rights Reserved.

Directions

Choose the item that best answers each question about the selection you just read. Fill in the circle next to the answer.

13 Compared to Jen, Lindsay is

○ happier.

○ sadder.

○ less afraid.

○ more afraid.

14 Based on Jen's second speech, what does Jen think of Lindsay?

○ that Lindsay is worrying too much

○ that Lindsay is cool for having a sleepover

○ that Lindsay is afraid of her brother

○ that Lindsay tells good ghost stories

15 Which character most wants to tell scary stories?

○ Lindsay

○ Jen

○ David

○ Lindsay's mom

16 Lindsay is angry at David because

○ it's a girls-only sleepover.

○ the tree house isn't big enough.

○ he scared her.

○ he's too young to play.

17 Which of the following events happens first?

○ Lindsay hides under a blanket.

○ Jen says she wants to tell ghost stories.

○ A loud bump shakes the tree house.

○ Lindsay wants to go inside and watch TV.

18 *The Tree House* is a good title because

○ the conflict is between Lindsay and nature.

○ a tree house is the setting of the script.

○ it tells the reader that the script will be scary.

○ the script describes what happens in all trees.

19 What conclusion can you draw about David?

○ He may have meant to scare Lindsay.

○ He came to bring his sister a snack.

○ He often wanders about in the dark.

○ He is much younger than Lindsay.

20 What effect does seeing David have on Lindsay?

○ She is still afraid of the dark.

○ She does not want to tell scary stories.

○ She tells David to go back in the house.

○ She tries to hide that she was afraid of him.

3 Copyright © Pearson Education, Inc., or its affiliates. All Rights Reserved.

GO ON

Name _____

WRITTEN RESPONSE TO THE SELECTION

> **Look Back and Write** Look back through the play to find out how the myth explains something in nature. Use details about the characters, setting, plot, and theme of the play to support your answer.

The information in the box below will help you remember what you should think about when you write your composition.

REMEMBER—YOU SHOULD

☐ tell how the myth explains something in nature.

☐ make sure you support your answer with details about the characters, setting, plot, and theme of the play.

☐ make sure that your explanation is clear enough for the reader to understand.

☐ try to use correct spelling, capitalization, punctuation, grammar, and sentences.

3 Copyright © Pearson Education, Inc., or its affiliates. All Rights Reserved.

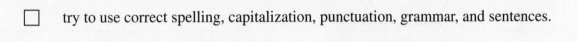

GO ON

3 Copyright © Pearson Education, Inc., or its affiliates. All Rights Reserved.

VOCABULARY

Directions

Find the word or words with the same meaning as the underlined word. Fill in the circle next to the answer.

1 The theater became <u>dim</u> before the start of the play.

- ○ very bright
- ○ crowded
- ○ small
- ○ somewhat dark

2 Kim, please pass me the <u>ladle</u>.

- ○ large spoon
- ○ kind of pen
- ○ sharp knife
- ○ rain jacket

3 The <u>temperature</u> is rising.

- ○ water level
- ○ balloon
- ○ amount of heat
- ○ building height

4 The blankets have different <u>patterns</u>.

- ○ sizes
- ○ shapes
- ○ weights
- ○ designs

5 The animal's eyes <u>shine</u> in the dark.

- ○ blink quickly
- ○ give off light
- ○ turn bright red
- ○ close tightly

6 A <u>gigantic</u> ship docked in the port.

- ○ very large
- ○ a lot of fun
- ○ out of control
- ○ ship for giants

7 The room was filled with <u>gas</u>.

- ○ liquids mixed together
- ○ old objects
- ○ lots of noise
- ○ an airlike substance

3 Copyright © Pearson Education, Inc., or its affiliates. All Rights Reserved.

GO ON

PHONICS

Directions
Find the word with the same consonant sound as the underlined word. Fill in the circle next to the answer.

8 I've been awake <u>since</u> six o'clock this morning.

Which word has the same sound as the <u>c</u> in <u>since</u>?

○ pink
○ ice
○ cart
○ rise

9 My <u>school</u> is down the street from me.

Which word has the same sound as the <u>ch</u> in <u>school</u>?

○ choose
○ match
○ pack
○ nice

10 I want the <u>large</u> box.

Which word has the same sound as the <u>ge</u> in <u>large</u>?

○ joke
○ shall
○ each
○ argue

11 An eagle dived off the <u>ledge</u> and into the air.

Which word has the same sound as the <u>dge</u> in <u>ledge</u>?

○ sugar
○ read
○ age
○ ranch

12 Draw a <u>circle</u> on the page.

Which word has the same sound as the second <u>c</u> in <u>circle</u>?

○ chilly
○ rice
○ days
○ cat

3 Copyright © Pearson Education, Inc., or its affiliates. All Rights Reserved.

COMPREHENSION

The Art of Painting

Then and Now

Early man painted on the walls of caves. Some of these cave paintings have been found to be as much as 17,000 years old. Today, painters do not paint on cave walls. But they still use pictures to try to communicate something about life.

Preparing to Paint

To begin, you need a paintbrush, paint, and a surface. Many painters paint on *canvas*. Canvas is a kind of heavy cloth like what is used for boat sails and tents. Painters join the canvas to a *stretcher*. A stretcher is a wood square frame that helps make the canvas tight.

Many painters use oil paint. Oil paint has *pigment*, or powdered color, mixed into the oil. Oil paint is popular because it dries slowly. But oil paint also eats away at canvas. For this reason, painters have to cover the canvas with *gesso* before they paint. Gesso is a type of glue that helps make the canvas smooth.

Mixing Colors

Before you paint, you have to decide what colors you will use and mix your paint. A set of paints usually has only three colors—red, blue, and yellow—the *primary colors*. Combinations of these three colors can create all the other colors. For example, yellow and blue make green. Red and blue make purple. Purple and yellow make brown.

Making A Picture

Now it is time to start putting marks on the canvas. Painters have different styles. Some painters try to paint in a *realistic style*. This means they paint things as they are in the real world. Others try to paint in an *impressionistic style*. This means they paint things as they seem to the painter. All painters think about shapes, color, and motion while they paint.

How to Look at Paintings

Painters do not always know what their pictures are about until after they've finished. A picture might tell a story. When you understand what the story is, you can understand what a painting means. Sometimes the same painting means different things to different people.

GO ON

3 Copyright © Pearson Education, Inc., or its affiliates. All Rights Reserved.

Directions

Choose the item that best answers each question about the selection you just read. Fill in the circle next to the answer.

13 What is the author's purpose in paragraph 1?

○ to explain why early humans painted on cave walls

○ to express the beauty of cave paintings

○ to tell visitors how to tour the art of old caves

○ to describe the historical importance of painting

14 The paragraphs under the heading Preparing to Paint give information about

○ steps to take before starting to paint.

○ the different ways to mix colors.

○ comparing and contrasting oil paints.

○ how to find meaning in paintings.

15 Which of the following is *not* a primary color?

○ red

○ blue

○ green

○ yellow

16 Under which heading would you expect to learn about how to make marks on a canvas?

○ Then and Now

○ Preparing to Paint

○ Mixing Colors

○ Making A Picture

17 According to the selection, how are painters alike?

○ They practice painting on cave walls.

○ They try to communicate something about life.

○ They have the same style.

○ They spend the same amount of time painting.

18 Which of the following words under the heading "Preparing to Paint" means "powdered color"?

○ canvas

○ stretcher

○ pigment

○ gesso

19 Which of the following steps comes first in painting?

○ putting marks on the canvas

○ covering the canvas with gesso

○ mixing primary colors

○ joining the canvas to a stretcher

20 Under which heading can you find information about understanding paintings?

○ How to Look at Paintings

○ Preparing to Paint

○ Then and Now

○ Making A Picture

3 Copyright © Pearson Education, Inc., or its affiliates. All Rights Reserved.

GO ON

WRITTEN RESPONSE TO THE SELECTION

Look Back and Write Look back at pages 450–454. Why do you see different constellations depending on where you live? Provide evidence to support your answer.

The information in the box below will help you remember what you should think about when you write your composition.

REMEMBER—YOU SHOULD

☐ explain why you see different constellations depending on where you live.

☐ provide evidence from the text to support your ideas.

☐ organize your ideas as you write to make your explanation clear to the reader.

☐ try to use correct spelling, capitalization, punctuation, grammar, and sentences.

3 Copyright © Pearson Education, Inc., or its affiliates. All Rights Reserved.

GO ON

Copyright © Pearson Education, Inc., or its affiliates. All Rights Reserved.

VOCABULARY

Directions

Find the word or words with the same meaning as the underlined word. Fill in the circle next to the answer.

1 He waited <u>anxiously</u> by the phone.

- ○ sleepily
- ○ nervously
- ○ happily
- ○ hopefully

2 The sun rose over the <u>bay</u>.

- ○ a dry section of the earth
- ○ a tall range of mountains
- ○ a channel between two seas
- ○ a small part of the ocean

3 We had three <u>blizzards</u> last year.

- ○ months that were icy
- ○ different tires with leaks
- ○ storms with a lot of snow
- ○ days that schools were closed

4 Rachel <u>chipped</u> away the ice.

- ○ broke off
- ○ grew
- ○ yelled at
- ○ wiggled

5 Paul could not hear the <u>melody</u>.

- ○ bell
- ○ whistle
- ○ tune
- ○ alarm

6 We put the <u>supplies</u> in the closet.

- ○ materials
- ○ laundry
- ○ books
- ○ yarn

7 Mrs. Dolan took us to hear the <u>symphony</u>.

- ○ rock concert
- ○ guest speaker
- ○ orchestra music
- ○ whale songs

3 Copyright © Pearson Education, Inc., or its affiliates. All Rights Reserved.

GO ON

WORD ANALYSIS

Directions

Find the suffix in the underlined word. Fill in the circle next to the answer.

8 Josie felt that winning the contest was <u>hopeless</u>.

○ s
○ hope
○ ess
○ less

9 We are learning to practice <u>kindness</u>.

○ ess
○ ness
○ kin
○ kind

10 Summer is <u>finally</u> here.

○ ly
○ lly
○ final
○ fin

11 Those flowers are <u>beautiful</u>.

○ be
○ beau
○ iful
○ ful

12 Marta <u>kindly</u> offered to help her grandmother.

○ kind
○ kin
○ ly
○ y

3 Copyright © Pearson Education, Inc., or its affiliates. All Rights Reserved.

GO ON

COMPREHENSION

Rocky Beach

"There's nothing to do," Lisa complained. It was the third day that she was stuck on vacation with her family. They were staying in a small, dark cabin made entirely of wooden logs. There was no radio and no television, but even worse, all of her friends were miles away.

"It's a beautiful day," said Lisa's dad. "I'm sure we can find something fun to do."

"There's nothing but trees, bugs, and more trees," Lisa said.

"Why don't we go to the lake today?" her dad suggested. A short walk from the cabin was a lake with an island in the middle. Lisa's dad had pointed out the lake when they arrived, but it was dark, and she couldn't see anything.

"Fine," said Lisa, "but I promise I'm not going to have any fun."

Lisa and her dad walked down a narrow gravel road and then along a small dirt path. The path stopped at a beach that curved around the edge of the lake.

The beach wasn't like any beach that Lisa had ever seen. Instead of sand, it was all rocks of different sizes, shapes, and colors. Lisa was glad she was wearing sneakers. She walked carefully over the rocks as they shifted under her weight.

"Look, Dad!" she cried, bending to pick up a red, swirled rock. She held it in her palm and then bent down to pick up a flat, black rock.

Lisa's dad followed her down to the rocks. He picked up a brown one and ran his thumb along its smooth outer edge.

"We can walk along the beach," Lisa's dad said, "and look for more rocks." They walked along the edge of the water comparing rocks until it began to grow dark.

"Can we come back tomorrow?" Lisa asked as she scrambled up to the path, still gripping the red rock in her palm.

3 Copyright © Pearson Education, Inc., or its affiliates. All Rights Reserved.

GO ON

Directions

Choose the item that best answers each question about the selection you just read. Fill in the circle next to the answer.

13 What generalization does Lisa make in paragraph 1?

- ○ She is staying in a cabin.
- ○ There is nothing to do on vacation.
- ○ She is far away from her friends.
- ○ She doesn't like to watch television.

14 Compared to Lisa, her dad is

- ○ unhappy to be on vacation.
- ○ bored by looking at the rocks.
- ○ able to find fun things to do.
- ○ more interested in staying in the cabin.

15 In paragraph 4, what generalization does Lisa's father make?

- ○ Lisa needs something to do.
- ○ Short walks lead to lakes.
- ○ There's nothing else to do.
- ○ The weather won't be good later.

16 Where do Lisa and her father go in paragraph 6?

- ○ to the cabin
- ○ to the woods
- ○ to a lake
- ○ to an island

17 What general statement can be made about the beach in paragraph 7?

- ○ It is sandy.
- ○ It isn't very big.
- ○ It isn't safe.
- ○ It is all rocks.

18 What generalization can you make about Lisa?

- ○ Lisa doesn't like to watch television.
- ○ Lisa likes looking at rocks.
- ○ Lisa thinks the beach is boring.
- ○ Lisa thinks the lake is big.

19 At the end of the passage, what can you conclude about Lisa?

- ○ She wants to come back the next day.
- ○ She wants to go home.
- ○ She doesn't like the cabin.
- ○ She likes being on vacation.

20 What generalization can you make from this vacation?

- ○ Vacations in winter are more fun than vacations in summer.
- ○ There are many things to do in nature.
- ○ You need television, radio, and friends to have fun.
- ○ There are rocks at all beaches.

3 Copyright © Pearson Education, Inc., or its affiliates. All Rights Reserved.

WRITTEN RESPONSE TO THE SELECTION

> **Look Back and Write** The old ones talk about "other music." What is the "other music," and why is it important? Use story details to support your answer.

The information in the box below will help you remember what you should think about when you write your composition.

REMEMBER—YOU SHOULD

☐ explain what the "other music" is and why it is important.

☐ use details from the story to support your ideas.

☐ make sure that each sentence you write is clear and understandable to the reader.

☐ try to use correct spelling, capitalization, punctuation, grammar, and sentences.

---

3 Copyright © Pearson Education, Inc., or its affiliates. All Rights Reserved.

3 Copyright © Pearson Education, Inc., or its affiliates. All Rights Reserved.

VOCABULARY

Directions

Find the word or words with the same meaning as the underlined word. Fill in the circle next to the answer.

1 First she noticed the bee, and then she felt the **stinging**.

○ pleasant pinch
○ soft bite
○ painful prick
○ icy snap

2 The **topic** of the speech was the history of the town.

○ subject
○ detail
○ search
○ conclusion

3 After spending a night on a boat, the **survivors** made it to dry land.

○ people that are hurt
○ people that know how to swim
○ people that go on vacation
○ people that remain alive

4 Granddad's cheers were an **unseen** force that helped me win the race.

○ missing
○ hidden
○ absent
○ lofty

5 A **noble** person is usually thoughtful to others.

○ having great qualities
○ having grown up rich
○ having a great education
○ having traveled the world

6 We took the car through the new **waterless** carwash.

○ not needing soap
○ good for the environment
○ without water
○ thirsty

7 Jessie's excuse for being late was **incredible**.

○ really funny
○ obviously a lie
○ weird
○ hard to believe

3 Copyright © Pearson Education, Inc., or its affiliates. All Rights Reserved.

PHONICS

Directions
Find the word that best answers each question. Fill in the circle next to the answer.

8 I got the last two answers <u>wrong</u>!

Which word has the same sound as the <u>wr</u> in <u>wrong</u>?

- ○ wing
- ○ run
- ○ with
- ○ white

9 The snow <u>glistens</u> in the sun.

Which word has the same sound as the <u>st</u> in <u>glistens</u>?

- ○ kiss
- ○ sugar
- ○ shout
- ○ team

10 Let's <u>climb</u> to the top of the hill.

Which word has the same sound as the <u>mb</u> in <u>climb</u>?

- ○ club
- ○ bone
- ○ cling
- ○ umpire

11 The dog <u>gnaws</u> her bone.

Which word has the same sound as the <u>gn</u> in <u>gnaws</u>?

- ○ game
- ○ grow
- ○ wag
- ○ name

12 My greasy hands keep slipping off the <u>doorknob</u>.

Which word has the same sound as the <u>kn</u> in <u>doorknob</u>?

- ○ dock
- ○ cob
- ○ noon
- ○ kidding

COMPREHENSION

At the Top

Mount Kilimanjaro is a mountain in Africa. Actually, it's a special type of mountain called an inactive volcano. At 19,340 feet, it is the highest peak in Africa.

Mount Kilimanjaro is located near the equator. It is usually very hot close to the equator because the sun shines more directly there than most other places on Earth. But because Mount Kilimanjaro is so high, it is very cold at the top.

GO ON

3 Copyright © Pearson Education, Inc., or its affiliates. All Rights Reserved.

The base of the volcano is wet and covered with green trees. But at the top there is a large glacier of ice, and it snows often.

Many people have climbed all the way to the top of Mount Kilimanjaro. These hikers, along with other scientists, have seen how the mountain has changed over the years. The first European climbed the mountain more than one hundred years ago and wrote about how much ice was at the top.

Today, almost all of that ice is gone. The glacier is getting smaller, leaving behind rocks that slide down the sides of the peak.

Some people think that humans are causing temperature changes that make the ice melt. Other people say the ice has been melting for a very long time. They think the melting is natural because it happened before the Earth's temperature started to change.

Scientists continue to look at the ice on Kilimanjaro to see how fast it is melting. They want to study how the mountain is changing to see how those changes will affect the people, plants, and animals that live around it.

People are also interested in Kilimanjaro because it is different from other places on Earth. They like to see pictures of the mountain and learn about the different living things that surround it.

Directions
Choose the item that best answers each question about the selection you just read. Fill in the circle next to the answer.

13 **What is the effect of the sun on temperatures near the equator?**

○ Because the sun shines directly, temperatures are hot.

○ Because the sun shines at an angle, temperatures vary greatly.

○ Because the sun shines at an angle, it snows often.

○ Because the sun shines directly, glaciers melt.

14 **What causes the cold temperatures at the top of Mount Kilimanjaro?**

○ the angle of the sun as it hits the top of the mountain

○ the large glacier at the top of the mountain

○ the extreme height of the mountain

○ the mountain's location near the equator

GO ON

3 Copyright © Pearson Education, Inc., or its affiliates. All Rights Reserved.

15 What is the cause of rocks sliding down the sides of the mountain's peak?

○ The angle of the sun at the equator has changed.

○ Scientific equipment has affected the glacier.

○ Human traffic has melted the ice.

○ The glacier at the top is getting smaller.

16 Which of the following is a generalization made in paragraph 6?

○ Human activity may be causing the ice to melt.

○ The ice will return when the temperatures change back.

○ When the ice is gone, Mount Kilimanjaro will be prettier.

○ Temperatures near the equator are unchanged.

17 Some people think that the melting of the ice is natural because

○ scientists have been studying changes on the mountain.

○ humans are causing temperatures to change everywhere.

○ it happened before the Earth's temperature started to change.

○ the melting ice affects people, plants, and animals.

18 What is one result of the melting ice on Kilimanjaro?

○ It is much easier to climb.

○ Many different living things are affected.

○ Scientists can finally agree on what to study.

○ It no longer snows at the top.

19 Which of the following is a fact given in the selection?

○ Kilimanjaro is the highest peak in Africa.

○ Kilimanjaro is an interesting volcano.

○ Kilimanjaro is the best mountain to climb.

○ Kilimanjaro is not very interesting to learn about.

20 After reading the selection, what can you conclude about Mount Kilimanjaro?

○ There is no reason to study Kilimanjaro because it isn't changing.

○ There are many reasons that people want to study Kilimanjaro.

○ We can't learn any more about Kilimanjaro until it erupts.

○ We won't be able to study Kilimanjaro until all the ice melts.

3 Copyright © Pearson Education, Inc., or its affiliates. All Rights Reserved.

WRITTEN RESPONSE TO THE SELECTION

Look Back and Write Look back at page 521. Which animals do you think are dangerous? Provide evidence to support your answer.

The information in the box below will help you remember what you should think about when you write your composition.

REMEMBER—YOU SHOULD

☐ tell which animals are dangerous.

☐ use details from the text as evidence to support your answer.

☐ write about your ideas in detail so that the reader understands why you think the animals are dangerous.

☐ try to use correct spelling, capitalization, punctuation, grammar, and sentences.

3 Copyright © Pearson Education, Inc., or its affiliates. All Rights Reserved.

GO ON

_____

_____

_____

_____

_____

_____

_____

_____

_____

_____

_____

_____

_____

_____

_____

_____

_____

_____

_____

_____

_____

3 Copyright © Pearson Education, Inc., or its affiliates. All Rights Reserved.

VOCABULARY

Directions

Find the word or words with the same meaning as the underlined word. Fill in the circle next to the answer.

1 **Plants left outside will freeze tonight.**

○ need water

○ be kept from spoiling

○ harden into ice

○ be protected from cold

2 **It's not safe to drive in terrible weather.**

○ dark

○ slippery

○ lovely

○ very bad

3 **Giles looked forward to middle school sports.**

○ athletic games

○ teamwork

○ health

○ basketball

4 **Strawberry is a popular flavor of ice-cream.**

○ boring

○ traditional

○ well-liked

○ uncommon

5 **Mary got up early to study for the test.**

○ learn carefully

○ solve problems

○ practice writing

○ make excuses

6 **The doctors learned that the disease can be treated.**

○ wellness

○ medicine

○ research

○ sickness

7 **The guard scored twelve points in the game.**

○ player with the most trophies

○ basketball player at the back of the court

○ official keeping score during the game

○ oldest player on the team

3 Copyright © Pearson Education, Inc., or its affiliates. All Rights Reserved.

GO ON

WORD ANALYSIS

Directions
Find the correct plural form of the underlined word. Fill in the circle next to the answer.

8 The <u>woman</u> is wearing a blue dress.

- ○ womans
- ○ women
- ○ womens
- ○ womanes

9 I need a <u>knife</u> to cut the sandwich.

- ○ knifes
- ○ knivs
- ○ knifs
- ○ knives

10 When it's snowing, Jenny always wears her <u>scarf</u>.

- ○ scarfs
- ○ scarves
- ○ scarfes
- ○ scarvs

11 The <u>child</u> was too small to go on the ride.

- ○ childrens
- ○ childs
- ○ children
- ○ childes

12 Johnny tripped when his <u>foot</u> got caught on his scooter.

- ○ feet
- ○ foots
- ○ footes
- ○ feets

COMPREHENSION

Becoming a Good Dancer

An Old Art Form

Dancing is one of the oldest art forms. Throughout history, people have danced as a way to express their ideas, emotions, and beliefs. Dancing is no different today. People still dance as a way to communicate. Dancing can be formal or casual. Either way, dancing is one of the most enjoyable ways to spend time. And anyone can learn!

GO ON

3 Copyright © Pearson Education, Inc., or its affiliates. All Rights Reserved.

Practice Makes Perfect

Once you've learned how to dance, you never forget. Dancing is like riding a bike or having a conversation with a friend. Analyzing what you're doing gets in the way of feeling it naturally. To be a good dancer, you have to learn to move to the music without thinking. Instead of anticipating each step before you make it, teach your feet to respond to the music. How do you teach your feet to move without thinking? Practice!

How to Practice

Dancing is about the repetition of basic steps. Beginners must be willing to make mistakes. The best way to start is without music. Dance alone in your room. Go over the steps again and again until the repetition feels effortless. Once you can do the steps, practice them with very slow music. As you improve, you can practice to a faster song. Dance with a partner only after you are comfortable performing the steps alone and with music.

After you know the basics, one of the easiest ways to master additional dance steps is with good friends before a party. Get a group together, put on some favorite music, and dance. Watch your friends to see which moves they know, and ask them to teach you.

The Benefits of Dancing

There are countless benefits to dancing. Good dancers enjoy the happiness that only dancing can bring. Dancing is fun. Dancing together helps people get to know one another. It also helps us enjoy music in a new way. One of the greatest advantages to dancing is that it's good exercise.

Different Types of Dancing

There are as many different types of dancing as there are different types of music. Each country in the world has its traditional dances. No dance is better than any other, but dances can mean different things. Remember, dancing is a form of self-expression. The style of dancing you enjoy says a lot about who you are.

3 Copyright © Pearson Education, Inc., or its affiliates. All Rights Reserved.

COMPREHENSION

Directions

Choose the item that best answers each question about the selection you just read. Fill in the circle next to the answer.

13 What generalization does the author make in paragraph 1?

○ Dancing is difficult for some people to learn.

○ Throughout history, dance music has not changed.

○ The steps of popular dances have not changed.

○ The purpose of dancing has not changed.

14 What generalization does the author make in paragraph 2?

○ Good dancers don't think about the steps.

○ Bike riders are also good dancers.

○ Practice gets in the way of dancing.

○ Good dancers plan each step in advance.

15 The first step in learning how to dance is

○ watching professional dancers.

○ putting on your favorite music.

○ being willing to make mistakes.

○ gathering a group of good friends.

16 Which of the following is a generalization the author makes under the heading How to Practice?

○ The best way to start is with a partner.

○ The worst way to master new steps is alone.

○ The best way to start is without music.

○ The easiest way to practice is after a party.

17 Which detail supports the main idea that there are many benefits to dancing?

○ Dancing is good exercise.

○ Dancers don't have to think.

○ Good dancers don't have to practice.

○ Dancing is about repetition of basic steps.

18 What is a generalization the author makes in paragraph 5?

○ Most people dance because it is easy.

○ Dancing is a great way to meet new people.

○ Dancing is good for the heart.

○ Dancing brings a special kind of happiness.

19 What fact in paragraph 6 lets you generalize that dancing is a part of a country's culture?

○ No dance is better than any other.

○ Each country in the world has traditional dances.

○ Dancing is a form of self-expression.

○ Different dances match different types of music.

20 Based on the headings, in which paragraph would you expect to learn about the specific methods for learning to dance?

○ paragraph 1

○ paragraph 3

○ paragraph 5

○ paragraph 6

GO ON

3 Copyright © Pearson Education, Inc., or its affiliates. All Rights Reserved.

WRITTEN RESPONSE TO THE SELECTION

Look Back and Write Look back through the selection to find facts and details about the character of James Naismith. Write about what traits helped him become a success in his life. Provide evidence to support your answer.

The information in the box below will help you remember what you should think about when you write your composition.

REMEMBER—YOU SHOULD

☐ explain what traits helped James Naismith become a success in life.

☐ support your explanation with details from the text.

☐ make sure that each sentence you write helps the reader understand your composition.

☐ try to use correct spelling, capitalization, punctuation, grammar, and sentences.

3 Copyright © Pearson Education, Inc., or its affiliates. All Rights Reserved.

GO ON

3 Copyright © Pearson Education, Inc., or its affiliates. All Rights Reserved.

VOCABULARY

Directions
Find the word or words with the same meaning as the underlined word. Fill in the circle next to the answer.

1 It was difficult to measure the pond's __depth.__

- ○ color
- ○ deepness
- ○ coolness
- ○ shape

2 Lee's dog was the __average__ size.

- ○ real
- ○ large
- ○ common
- ○ correct

3 The swift __tides__ left many shells behind.

- ○ blast of wind
- ○ rise and fall of ocean water
- ○ speeding ships
- ○ ocean birds

4 Thick clouds hid the __peak.__

- ○ top of a mountain
- ○ side of a cliff
- ○ full moon
- ○ setting sun

5 Life in the __desert__ is hard.

- ○ place with many forests
- ○ big city
- ○ place that is very dry
- ○ dark cave

6 We saw many beautiful __waterfalls.__

- ○ tumbling waterways
- ○ frozen streams
- ○ large lakes
- ○ long rivers

7 Bill can __outrun__ Alex.

- ○ throw farther than
- ○ yell louder than
- ○ run faster than
- ○ jump higher than

3 Copyright © Pearson Education, Inc., or its affiliates. All Rights Reserved.

GO ON

WORD ANALYSIS

*D*irections

Find the word with the same *r*-controlled vowel sound as the underlined word. Fill in the circle next to the answer.

8 A light <u>appeared</u> in front of Paulie.

Which word has the same sound as the <u>ear</u> in <u>appeared</u>?

○ over
○ hard
○ learn
○ beard

9 Where in the <u>world</u> is that cat?

Which word has the same sound as the <u>or</u> in <u>world</u>?

○ ford
○ feared
○ whole
○ early

10 Joe has a guitar lesson every <u>Thursday</u>.

Which word has the same sound as the <u>ur</u> in <u>Thursday</u>?

○ worm
○ four
○ throw
○ wear

11 Betsy was <u>dirty</u> after playing in the park.

Which word has the same sound as the <u>ir</u> in <u>dirty</u>?

○ pretty
○ more
○ nerve
○ tire

12 Andy got a <u>perfect</u> score in his spelling test.

Which word has the same sound as the <u>er</u> in <u>perfect</u>?

○ earth
○ there
○ partly
○ berry

COMPREHENSION

Seven Summits in Seven Months

Climbing Everest, the highest mountain in the world, is amazing. Climbing the highest mountain on each of the seven continents is even more amazing. Now think about climbing the highest mountain on each of the seven continents in just seven months. That has to be one of the most amazing things ever!

In April 1985, an American named Richard Bass made it to the top of Everest.

GO ON

3 Copyright © Pearson Education, Inc., or its affiliates. All Rights Reserved.

That was the day Bass reached his goal of climbing all Seven Summits. Seven Summits is the term used for the tallest mountain on each continent. It took Richard Bass a few years to reach that goal.

In 1990, New Zealanders Rob Hall and Gary Ball set an even harder goal for themselves. They wanted to climb all Seven Summits in just seven months! They began with Everest in May, and they finished in December by making it to the top of Vinson in Antarctica. They did it with just six hours to spare!

Sadly, both Rob Hall and Gary Ball have died since their amazing seven-month adventure. In 1993, Ball died of a swelling in his brain while climbing another mountain in Asia. Hall was making another trip up Everest in 1996 when he got caught in a snowstorm and died near the summit.

It's been more than twenty years since Richard Bass's Seven Summits journey. Since that time, more than one hundred other people have climbed their way to the top of every continent.

BASS'S LIST OF THE SEVEN SUMMITS		
Continent	**Mountain**	**Height in Feet**
Asia	Everest	29,035
South America	Aconcagua	22,834
North America	McKinley (Denali)	20,320
Africa	Kilimanjaro	19,340
Europe	Elbrus	18,510
Antarctica	Vinson	16,066
Australia	Kosciuszko	7,310

Directions
Choose the item that best answers each question about the selection you just read. Fill in the circle next to the answer.

3 Copyright © Pearson Education, Inc., or its affiliates. All Rights Reserved.

13 Which continent is home to the highest mountain?

○ North America
○ South America
○ Australia
○ Asia

14 Only one of the Seven Summits is less than 10,000 feet tall. Which one?

○ Kosciuszko
○ Kilimanjaro
○ Elbrus
○ Vinson

GO ON

15 Which mountain is on the continent of Europe?

○ Aconcagua

○ Everest

○ Elbrus

○ Kilimanjaro

16 What is the difference in height between Everest and McKinley?

○ more than 10,000 feet

○ almost 9,000 feet

○ less than 5,000 feet

○ exactly 9,000 feet

17 Antarctica's Vinson is higher than only one other mountain on the chart. Which one?

○ Kilimanjaro

○ Everest

○ Kosciuszko

○ Elbrus

18 Which fact does NOT support the main idea that climbing the Seven Summits in seven months is amazing?

○ The Seven Summits range in height from 7,310 to 29,035 feet.

○ The Seven Summits are all on different continents.

○ More than one hundred people have climbed the Seven Summits.

○ Everest is the highest mountain in the world.

19 In what year did Rob Hall and Gary Ball complete the Seven Summits?

○ 1993

○ 1985

○ 1990

○ 1996

20 How many other climbers have climbed the Seven Summits?

○ more than one hundred

○ less than one hundred

○ exactly one hundred

○ Only Richard Bass, Rob Hall, and Gary Ball have been able to do it.

3   Copyright © Pearson Education, Inc., or its affiliates. All Rights Reserved.

GO ON

WRITTEN RESPONSE TO THE SELECTION

> **Look Back and Write** Mt. Everest is the highest mountain, but Kauna Kea is the tallest mountain. Look back at page 67. Write the reason that the tallest and the highest mountain are not the same. Provide evidence to support your answer.

The information in the box below will help you remember what you should think about when you write your composition.

REMEMBER—YOU SHOULD

☐ explain why the tallest and the highest mountain are not the same.

☐ make sure you provide evidence from the text to support your answer.

☐ make sure your writing is clear and well-organized.

☐ try to use correct spelling, capitalization, punctuation, grammar, and sentences.

---

3 Copyright © Pearson Education, Inc., or its affiliates. All Rights Reserved.

GO ON

3 Copyright © Pearson Education, Inc., or its affiliates. All Rights Reserved.

Name _____

VOCABULARY

*D*irections

Find the word or words with the same meaning as the underlined word. Fill in the circle next to the answer.

1 Brett needed more time to finish his <u>chores</u>.

- ○ tasks
- ○ meals
- ○ stories
- ○ songs

2 We couldn't find the <u>spare</u> tire.

- ○ rubber
- ○ small
- ○ extra
- ○ new

3 Mother said it was time to clean the <u>attic</u>.

- ○ cellar
- ○ backyard
- ○ front porch
- ○ top floor

4 Aunt Linda carefully <u>labeled</u> the jars.

- ○ sealed with a lid
- ○ marked with a tag
- ○ packed in a box
- ○ weighed on a scale

5 Each <u>customer</u> took a ticket.

- ○ person who helps other people
- ○ person who travels to faraway places
- ○ person who works in an office
- ○ person who buys something

6 The <u>board</u> voted for the new rules.

- ○ head group of people
- ○ flat piece of wood
- ○ children in a school
- ○ very large family

7 That package needs more <u>stamps</u>.

- ○ wrapping paper
- ○ tape
- ○ postage stickers
- ○ ribbons

3 Copyright © Pearson Education, Inc., or its affiliates. All Rights Reserved.

GO ON

WORD ANALYSIS

Directions

Find the word or words with the same meaning as the underlined word. Fill in the circle next to the answer.

8 The directions say to <u>premix</u> part of the cake.
- ◯ mix before
- ◯ mix things at the same time
- ◯ mix again
- ◯ mix after

9 While Mike's family was on vacation, their grass became <u>overgrown</u>.
- ◯ too short
- ◯ too long
- ◯ too wide
- ◯ too wet

10 Ron stayed up until <u>midnight</u> on New Year's Eve.
- ◯ dinner time
- ◯ the middle of the morning
- ◯ nap time
- ◯ the middle of the night

11 Janet has many friends because she is <u>outgoing</u>.
- ◯ pretty
- ◯ very friendly
- ◯ leaving the house
- ◯ shy

12 The train is ready to <u>depart</u>.
- ◯ arrive
- ◯ connect
- ◯ leave
- ◯ load

COMPREHENSION

Hurricanes

Hurricanes are large tropical storms that form over the oceans of the world. Small storms gather heat and energy from the warm ocean water. The heat from the water makes the storms stronger and bigger. Soon some of these storms can form into hurricanes. Hurricanes that stay over warm water can become even larger and more forceful, but they lose their power when they reach land.

Hurricanes are storms that get names. A new list of names is created each year. The first hurricane name starts with the letter A, like Amanda, and the names move through the

GO ON

3 Copyright © Pearson Education, Inc., or its affiliates. All Rights Reserved.

alphabet as more hurricanes appear. Sometimes it is strange to think of a dangerous storm having a person's name, but naming storms is a way to keep track of them.

Hurricane clouds move in a circle around a point called an eye. The eye is the center of the storm. In pictures of hurricanes, the eye is the scariest-looking part. To be called a hurricane, a storm must have winds of at least 74 miles per hour. But hurricanes can have winds of more than 120 miles per hour!

When a hurricane moves over land, there are heavy rains, large waves, and strong winds. These can cause much damage to buildings, cars, roads, and trees.

Also, flooding can occur when large waves called storm surges hit the beaches. Storm surges are the main reason people are told to leave their homes and move to higher ground during a hurricane.

Scientists who study the weather watch these storms very closely so they can tell people how strong they are and where they are going. In the United States, hurricane season lasts from June 1 to November 30. People who live near the ocean find hurricane season very stressful.

The National Hurricane Center says that everyone near the ocean should have a family plan for dealing with a hurricane. They should also have a supply kit. This kit has things that are useful in a disaster, such as tools, water, food, first aid, and clothing. But it says the best way to handle a hurricane is to leave town at the first reports of high winds.

Directions
Choose the item that best answers each question about the selection you just read. Fill in the circle next to the answer.

13 **Which generalization can you make about hurricanes based on the information in the passage?**

○ Hurricane season always lasts for two months.

○ Hurricanes are usually very small storms.

○ Hurricanes only stay over water.

○ All hurricanes move in a circle around a center point.

14 **Which of the following is an effect of storm surges?**

○ floods

○ strong winds

○ fires

○ heavy rains

3 Copyright © Pearson Education, Inc., or its affiliates. All Rights Reserved.

15 **What conclusion can you draw from the facts in paragraph 1?**

○ Hurricanes are the most forceful storms on Earth.

○ Large tropical storms are stronger than hurricanes.

○ Hurricanes that form over land are powerless.

○ The warmer the ocean water, the stronger the storm.

16 **Which of the following is an opinion found in paragraph 2?**

○ The first hurricane name starts with the letter A.

○ It can be strange to think of a dangerous storm with a name.

○ Naming storms is a way to keep track of them.

○ Hurricanes are storms that are given names.

17 **What conclusion can you draw from the facts in paragraph 3?**

○ The eye is the scariest part of a hurricane.

○ Hurricane clouds move straight past the eye.

○ A storm with 110 mile-an-hour winds is very strong.

○ Winds less than 74 miles per hour are ignored.

18 **Which of the following details supports the idea that hurricanes are harmful?**

○ All families have a supply kit.

○ Hurricanes damage buildings, cars, roads, and trees.

○ Scientists watch hurricanes.

○ Storm surges are large waves that hit the beaches.

19 **Which of the following is an opinion held by people who live near the ocean?**

○ Hurricanes can have winds of more than 120 miles per hour.

○ Hurricanes bring heavy rains.

○ August is the most dangerous month for hurricanes.

○ Hurricane season is very stressful.

20 **What conclusion can you draw from the facts in paragraph 7?**

○ During a hurricane, heavy rainfall comes before high winds.

○ The National Hurricane Center helps people prepare for hurricanes.

○ A supply kit has tools, water, food, and other useful things.

○ The best way to handle a hurricane is to leave town.

3 Copyright © Pearson Education, Inc., or its affiliates. All Rights Reserved.

GO ON

Name _____

WRITTEN RESPONSE TO THE SELECTION

> **Look Back and Write** Look back at pages 96–98. Use facts and details from the selection to write what the father collected and why. Provide evidence to support your answer.

The information in the box below will help you remember what you should think about when you write your composition.

REMEMBER—YOU SHOULD

☐ tell what the father collected and why he collected it.

☐ use facts and details from the text to provide evidence to support your answer.

☐ write about your ideas in detail so that the reader understands what you are saying.

☐ try to use correct spelling, capitalization, punctuation, grammar, and sentences.

3 Copyright © Pearson Education, Inc., or its affiliates. All Rights Reserved.

GO ON

Copyright © Pearson Education, Inc., or its affiliates. All Rights Reserved.

Name _____

VOCABULARY

Directions

Find the word or words with the same meaning as the underlined word. Fill in the circle next to the answer.

1 Three men fell off the boat and <u>drowned</u>.
- ○ breathed in water and died
- ○ swam away toward land
- ○ shouted for help
- ○ stayed together

2 The coach showed Allie some new <u>strokes</u>.
- ○ swimming clothes
- ○ places to swim
- ○ ways of swimming
- ○ names of swimmers

3 The wind <u>stirred</u> the leaves.
- ○ bored
- ○ thanked
- ○ warmed
- ○ moved

4 Mark proudly displayed his <u>medals</u>.
- ○ awards
- ○ grades
- ○ books
- ○ pictures

5 Laura <u>continued</u> to tell her story.
- ○ hated
- ○ sat down
- ○ refused
- ○ went on

6 We took the day off to <u>celebrate</u>.
- ○ rejoice
- ○ rest
- ○ go shopping
- ○ travel

7 Her raft was carried away by the <u>current</u>.
- ○ large fish
- ○ small bird
- ○ flow of water
- ○ wooden boat

3 Copyright © Pearson Education, Inc., or its affiliates. All Rights Reserved.

GO ON

WORD ANALYSIS

Directions

Fill in the circle next to the word that fills the blank.

8 A person who wants to teach becomes a _____.

- ○ teachor
- ○ teachist
- ○ teacher
- ○ teachess

9 When Jason goes to visit his grandmother, he is her _____.

- ○ visitor
- ○ visiter
- ○ advisor
- ○ visor

10 The female lion is called a _____.

- ○ liness
- ○ lioness
- ○ liner
- ○ lionist

11 When I tour another city, I pretend not to be a _____.

- ○ touress
- ○ touror
- ○ tourer
- ○ tourist

12 To conduct an orchestra, a _____ uses his or her arms.

- ○ conductor
- ○ conducter
- ○ conductist
- ○ convict

COMPREHENSION

Dorothy Hamill, Olympic Champion

Women's figure skating is one of the most exciting events in the Winter Olympics. It became an Olympic event in the 1924 games in France. In 1976, a nineteen-year-old American won the gold medal. Her name is Dorothy Hamill. At the time she was the greatest skater in the world.

Dorothy Hamill was born in 1956 in Chicago, Illinois. She has an older brother and sister. Shortly after she was born, Dorothy's family moved to Connecticut.

When Dorothy was eight, she went skating with her sister and a friend. She got upset when the other two girls were able to skate backwards. She was unable to do that and cried about it to her mom. Mrs. Hamill signed Dorothy up for skating lessons.

GO ON

3 Copyright © Pearson Education, Inc., or its affiliates. All Rights Reserved.

When she turned fourteen, Dorothy's family took her out of school so that she could skate more. She skated seven hours a day, six days a week. Private teachers helped Dorothy keep up with her schoolwork. Dorothy began training with a well-known skating coach, Carlo Fassi. Together they created Dorothy's famous move, the "Hamill Camel." This is a camel spin that turns into a sit spin. It was the best skating move ever created!

Dorothy won three national championship medals in a row before the 1976 Olympic Games in Austria. She won the gold medal and became an idol to girls all over America. Many girls showed their love by cutting their hair in Hamill's famous short haircut.

Later in 1976, Dorothy decided to turn pro. She joined the Ice Capades and was their star skater from 1977 to 1984. After the Ice Capades, Dorothy won four straight World Professional Figure Skating championships.

Hamill says she does not like to see videos of herself from her Olympic days. "I wasn't very good, not compared to what they can do today [or] to what I can do today. I don't think people realize that skaters get better as they get older."

Dorothy says of her success, "I worked as hard as I could. I was always the first one on the ice and the last one off."

Dorothy Hamill now lives in Baltimore, Maryland, with her daughter. She became a member of The Olympic Hall of Fame in 1996. It was the highest achievement of her career.

Directions

Choose the item that best answers each question about the selection you just read. Fill in the circle next to the answer.

13 **Which sentence from the selection is a statement of fact?**

- ○ It was the best skating move ever created!
- ○ Women's figure skating is one of the most exciting events in the Winter Olympics.
- ○ "I wasn't very good, not compared to what they can do today [or] to what I can do today."
- ○ Dorothy Hamill was born in 1956 in Chicago, Illinois.

14 **Which is a statement of opinion based on the selection?**

- ○ Dorothy Hamill turned pro in 1976.
- ○ Dorothy Hamill joined The Olympic Hall of Fame in 1996.
- ○ Dorothy Hamill was the greatest skater of the 1970s.
- ○ Dorothy Hamill began skating as a little girl.

GO ON

3 Copyright © Pearson Education, Inc., or its affiliates. All Rights Reserved.

15 Which sentence from the selection is a statement of opinion?

○ It was the highest achievement of her career.

○ Private teachers helped Dorothy keep up with her schoolwork.

○ Dorothy Hamill now lives in Baltimore, Maryland, with her daughter.

○ Dorothy began training with a well-known skating coach, Carlo Fassi.

16 Which is a statement of fact based on the selection?

○ Dorothy is a better skater today than she was in the 1970s.

○ Dorothy Hamill was in the Ice Capades for about seven years.

○ Everyone loved Dorothy's haircut.

○ No one could skate backwards better than Dorothy.

17 Which is a statement of opinion based on the selection?

○ After being in the Olympics, Dorothy Hamill turned pro.

○ Dorothy was the first American to get a gold medal for skating.

○ Skaters get better as they get older.

○ Dorothy won three national championships before winning the Olympic gold.

18 Which generalization can you make based on the selection?

○ Girls named Dorothy usually have short hair.

○ Dorothy Hamill worked hard and was a successful skater.

○ Having a private teacher is the best way to do well in school.

○ Figure skating was never popular before the Olympics.

19 What famous ice skating move did Dorothy Hamill invent with her coach?

○ the Flying Camel

○ the Hamill Giraffe

○ the Camel Spin

○ the Hamill Camel

20 When did figure skating become an Olympic event?

○ in 1924 in France

○ in 1942 in France

○ in 1956 in Chicago

○ in 1976 in Austria

3 Copyright © Pearson Education, Inc., or its affiliates. All Rights Reserved.

WRITTEN RESPONSE TO THE SELECTION

Look Back and Write Look back at the question on page 125. Write about Gertrude Ederle and how she surprised the world by being first. Provide evidence to support your answer.

The information in the box below will help you remember what you should think about when you write your composition.

REMEMBER—YOU SHOULD

☐   write about Gertrude Ederle and how she surprised the world by being first.

☐   use details from the text to support your ideas.

☐   organize your ideas clearly to help the reader understand your composition.

☐   try to use correct spelling, capitalization, punctuation, grammar, and sentences.

3 Copyright © Pearson Education, Inc., or its affiliates. All Rights Reserved.

3 Copyright © Pearson Education, Inc., or its affiliates. All Rights Reserved.

VOCABULARY

Directions

Find the word or words with the same meaning as the underlined word. Fill in the circle next to the answer.

1 A stream ran through the <u>valley</u>.

- ○ long, low land
- ○ deep, dark woods
- ○ green, rolling hills
- ○ steep, rocky cliff

2 The bird hid behind the <u>reeds</u>.

- ○ thick clouds
- ○ leafy trees
- ○ tall grasses
- ○ huge rocks

3 Dad's voice <u>echoed</u> in the hall.

- ○ was hard to hear
- ○ grew louder
- ○ fell silent
- ○ repeated

4 Rainwater rushed through the <u>gully</u>.

- ○ ditch
- ○ pipe
- ○ window
- ○ door

5 The boys <u>scrambled</u> over the hill.

- ○ pretend played
- ○ begged for help
- ○ looked through a telescope
- ○ climbed quickly

6 Donna <u>clutched</u> the bag in her hands.

- ○ held tight
- ○ closed
- ○ looked at
- ○ tore

7 We covered our fort with <u>thatch</u>.

- ○ cloth
- ○ plastic
- ○ plant material
- ○ paper

GO ON

3 Copyright © Pearson Education, Inc., or its affiliates. All Rights Reserved.

WORD ANALYSIS

Directions
For each underlined word, choose the item that shows how to divide it correctly into syllables. Fill in the circle next to the answer.

8 Sammy was sure there was a <u>monster</u> in her closet.

- ○ mo | nster
- ○ mons | ter
- ○ mon | ster
- ○ monst | er

9 We lined up at the <u>entrance</u> to the school.

- ○ en | trance
- ○ entr | ance
- ○ entran | ce
- ○ ent | rance

10 We are having a <u>surprise</u> party for Mike.

- ○ su | rprise
- ○ sur | prise
- ○ surpri | se
- ○ surp | rise

11 We need just three more pieces to <u>complete</u> the puzzle.

- ○ c | omplete
- ○ comp | lete
- ○ co | mplete
- ○ com | plete

12 Sandy and her <u>partner</u> finished before all the other teams.

- ○ part | ner
- ○ par | tner
- ○ partn | er
- ○ pa | rtner

COMPREHENSION

Training Ursula

Ursula never says anything. Her big eyes blink innocently. But I know she is sneaky because when I turn my head she does bad things. She climbs on the counter and unravels the paper towels. She steps on a chair and jumps out the window. Outside, she eats the plants or hides behind them so I can't find her. She harasses lizards and little birds. Or she climbs a tree, gets onto the roof, and can't get down.

Ursula is a beautiful cat. She has eyes that are the color of limes, dark fur that looks reddish in the sunlight, and a long, feathery tail that sticks straight up as she prowls around. But Ursula needs to be trained.

3 Copyright © Pearson Education, Inc., or its affiliates. All Rights Reserved.

GO ON

Because cats don't like water, one way to train them is with a water bottle. Every time Ursula began to eat my plants, I squirted her. But since Ursula's fur is so thick, the water never got to her skin. She continues to eat plants.

Another thing cats don't like is the smell of lemons and oranges. For this reason, I put orange oil on the windowsill that Ursula jumps out of. Did it work? No. Ursula found a way to open the front door with her paw.

Apparently, cats don't like to have their paws sticky. One book I read said to put sticky tape or glue on places where the cat shouldn't go. So I covered my counter with glue. Now my sandwich is glued to the counter and Ursula no longer unravels the paper towels. Instead, she unravels the toilet paper.

It remained a problem—Ursula chasing lizards and birds. Therefore, I went out and bought a cat leash. The directions on the box said that cat leashes are wonderful because they make it possible to stroll around the garden with your cat. That afternoon, I spent about an hour trying to put Ursula's little front legs into the harness. What do I have to show for it? Scratches up and down my arms.

I agreed to take Ursula from my friend Jorge who was moving out of town and had to leave her behind. Jorge said, "Cats are some of the most amazing animals on Earth." After a month living with Ursula, I have to agree with him. Cats are intelligent, stubborn, and independent. I've given up trying to train Ursula. Now I simply love her. With my new attitude, I find that the bad things Ursula does are less annoying. Cats have a great sense of humor.

Directions
Choose the item that best answers each question about the selection you just read. Fill in the circle next to the answer.

13 **Which of the following is *not* a cause of the author's need to train Ursula?**

○ Ursula unravels the paper towels.

○ Ursula jumps out the window.

○ Ursula is a beautiful cat.

○ Ursula gets on the roof.

14 **Which of the following helps paint a visual picture of the cat Ursula?**

○ Ursula's eyes are the color of limes.

○ Ursula is sneaky.

○ Ursula never says anything.

○ Ursula hides behind the plants.

GO ON

3 Copyright © Pearson Education, Inc., or its affiliates. All Rights Reserved.

15 Why does the author use a water bottle to try to train Ursula?

- ○ Cats have sharp claws.
- ○ Cats chase lizards.
- ○ Cats are intelligent.
- ○ Cats don't like water.

16 Which of the following is *not* an effect of the author putting glue on the counter?

- ○ The author's sandwich is glued to the counter.
- ○ Ursula unravels the toilet paper.
- ○ Ursula finds a way to open the front door.
- ○ Ursula no longer unravels the paper towels.

17 What is the *third* step the author takes to train Ursula?

- ○ The author buys a cat leash.
- ○ The author covers the counter with glue.
- ○ The author squirts Ursula with the water bottle.
- ○ The author covers the windowsill with orange oil.

18 What causes the author to buy a cat leash?

- ○ Ursula continues to chase lizards and birds.
- ○ The water never reaches Ursula's skin.
- ○ Ursula unravels the paper towels.
- ○ The glue on the counter didn't work.

19 What was the effect of the author's experiment with the cat leash?

- ○ Ursula stops chasing lizards and birds.
- ○ The author gives up on the water bottle.
- ○ The author gives up on the glue.
- ○ Ursula scratches the author's arms.

20 What conclusion can you draw by the end of the selection?

- ○ The author will give Ursula back to Jorge.
- ○ The author has come to understand cats.
- ○ The author keeps getting scratched by Ursula.
- ○ The author has covered the house with orange oil.

3 Copyright © Pearson Education, Inc., or its affiliates. All Rights Reserved.

GO ON

WRITTEN RESPONSE TO THE SELECTION

Look Back and Write Look back at pages 162–165. Write about why everyone thought the eagle was a chicken. Provide evidence to support your answer.

The information in the box below will help you remember what you should think about when you write your composition.

REMEMBER—YOU SHOULD

- ☐ explain why everyone thought the eagle was a chicken.

- ☐ use details from text as evidence to support your ideas.

- ☐ make sure the details you use are relevant to the topic.

- ☐ try to use correct spelling, capitalization, punctuation, grammar, and sentences.

3 Copyright © Pearson Education, Inc., or its affiliates. All Rights Reserved.

GO ON

_____

_____

_____

_____

_____

_____

_____

_____

_____

_____

_____

_____

_____

_____

_____

_____

_____

_____

_____

_____

_____

3 Copyright © Pearson Education, Inc., or its affiliates. All Rights Reserved.

VOCABULARY

Directions
Find the word or words with the same meaning as the underlined word. Fill in the circle next to the answer.

1 Kim moved three <u>paces</u> to the right.

- ⭕ seats
- ⭕ houses
- ⭕ steps
- ⭕ miles

2 James kept the <u>rhythm</u>.

- ⭕ handkerchief
- ⭕ prize
- ⭕ beat
- ⭕ secret

3 This is the winter <u>festival</u>.

- ⭕ show
- ⭕ meeting
- ⭕ storm
- ⭕ celebration

4 I wore my new <u>cotton</u> shirt.

- ⭕ cloth made from a plant
- ⭕ flower patterned
- ⭕ white and red colored
- ⭕ plant used to feed people

5 She looked <u>pale</u>.

- ⭕ red with anger
- ⭕ wrinkled with age
- ⭕ deep in thought
- ⭕ light in color

6 Mama was a <u>graceful</u> dancer.

- ⭕ beautiful
- ⭕ fast
- ⭕ careful
- ⭕ lively

7 My jacket is <u>snug</u>.

- ⭕ dirty
- ⭕ old
- ⭕ tight
- ⭕ long

GO ON

3   Copyright © Pearson Education, Inc., or its affiliates. All Rights Reserved.

WORD ANALYSIS

Directions

For each underlined word, choose the item that shows how to divide it correctly into syllables. Fill in the circle next to the answer.

8 When Mary plays the <u>piano</u>, I like to listen.

○ pia | no
○ pi | ano
○ pi | an | o
○ p | ia | no

9 The cowboy at the <u>rodeo</u> stayed on the bull for fifteen seconds.

○ ro | de | o
○ rod | eo
○ ro | deo
○ rode | o

10 The singer went to the music <u>studio</u> to record his new song.

○ st | udi | o
○ stu | di | o
○ stud | io
○ stu | dio

11 I like the <u>idea</u> of Daylight Savings Time because it stays light out longer.

○ i | d | ea
○ id | e | a
○ ide | a
○ i | de | a

12 The person who put cheese on a hamburger <u>created</u> a great meal.

○ cre | at | ed
○ cr | ea | ted
○ creat | ed
○ crea | t | ed

COMPREHENSION

Best Friends Learn a Lesson

Maggie and Kevin were best friends. They lived next door to each other on Maple Street in a small town named New Hope. They had a lot in common. They both loved climbing trees, collecting rocks, and riding scooters. They were both in the third grade at New Hope Elementary School. Both had Mrs. Harris as their teacher.

Unlike Kevin, Maggie loved to read. If she wasn't playing with Kevin, she could be found reading a book on her porch swing. Unlike Maggie, Kevin loved puzzles. His love of putting things together made Kevin very good at math. Maggie was not good at math.

Since the start of third grade, Kevin and Maggie had an agreement. After school, they would get together at one of their houses and begin their homework. Maggie

GO ON

3 Copyright © Pearson Education, Inc., or its affiliates. All Rights Reserved.

always let Kevin copy her spelling homework. She was such a good reader that spelling was her best subject. In return, Kevin always let Maggie copy his math homework.

This homework deal continued for the first two months of school. The leaves on Maple Street's trees had just begun to turn red when Mrs. Harris told her third graders that they would be tested in all subjects the next week.

Well, Maggie did poorly on her math test, and, of course, Kevin failed his spelling test! Mrs. Harris had a talk with both of them. She wanted to understand how it could be that they each did well on their homework but then did poorly on their tests.

Kevin and Maggie explained that they did their homework together after school. Kevin admitted that he copied Maggie's spelling while Maggie copied Kevin's math. Mrs. Harris told them that she was glad they told her the truth, and that they could both learn a lesson.

"I have an idea," said Mrs. Harris. "I think it's wonderful to work together after school, but it's bad to copy. By copying, neither of you is learning what you need to learn to do well in school. Maggie, spend some time helping Kevin with spelling so that he will become better. Kevin, you do the same for Maggie with math."

That's exactly what they did, and they learned that helping a friend to learn is better than letting a friend copy.

Directions
Choose the item that best answers each question about the selection you just read. Fill in the circle next to the answer.

13 **Which comparison best describes Maggie and Kevin?**

○ They have nothing in common.

○ They have one thing in common.

○ They have a few things in common.

○ They have a lot in common.

14 **Which interest do Maggie and Kevin share?**

○ They both live on Maple Street.

○ They both like New Hope Elementary School.

○ They both like rock collecting.

○ They both like playing soccer after school.

GO ON

3 Copyright © Pearson Education, Inc., or its affiliates. All Rights Reserved.

15 Unlike Kevin, what does Maggie like to do?

○ She likes to climb trees.

○ She likes to read.

○ She likes to do puzzles.

○ She likes to swing on the porch swing.

16 Unlike Maggie, what is Kevin good at?

○ reading

○ riding a scooter

○ math

○ spelling

17 How do Kevin and Maggie help each other with homework?

○ They copy from each other.

○ They answer each other's questions.

○ They go over the spelling homework together.

○ They review the math homework together.

18 What happens because Maggie and Kevin copy each other's homework?

○ Maggie and Kevin both get A's on their tests.

○ Maggie does poorly on her math test, and Kevin fails his spelling test.

○ Maggie and Kevin each get detention.

○ Mrs. Harris calls their parents, and they get punished at home.

19 What could Maggie usually be found doing if she wasn't playing with Kevin?

○ helping Mrs. Harris grade the tests

○ climbing trees

○ doing puzzles

○ reading a book on her porch swing

20 How will Kevin do on the next spelling test?

○ He will probably do better.

○ He will probably fail again.

○ He will definitely get an A+.

○ He will definitely fail.

3 Copyright © Pearson Education, Inc., or its affiliates. All Rights Reserved.

GO ON

WRITTEN RESPONSE TO THE SELECTION

> **Look Back and Write** Look back at the question on page 199. Think about the day Suki wore her kimono to the street festival. Now write a response to the question. Provide evidence to support your answer.

The information in the box below will help you remember what you should think about when you write your composition.

REMEMBER—YOU SHOULD

☐ explain how culture influenced the clothes that Suki wore to the street festival.

☐ find details in the story that support your answer to the question.

☐ use colorful describing words to make your writing interesting for the reader.

☐ try to use correct spelling, capitalization, punctuation, grammar, and sentences.

---

3 Copyright © Pearson Education, Inc., or its affiliates. All Rights Reserved.

3 Copyright © Pearson Education, Inc., or its affiliates. All Rights Reserved.

VOCABULARY

Directions
Find the word or words with the same meaning as the underlined word. Fill in the circle next to the answer.

1 We are going to the <u>circus</u>.
- ◯ a clothing store
- ◯ a traveling show
- ◯ an outdoor play
- ◯ a big parade

2 The story was <u>difficult</u>.
- ◯ made up
- ◯ long
- ◯ hard to understand
- ◯ illustrated

3 The kids are <u>nibbling</u> their food.
- ◯ playing with food
- ◯ throwing food
- ◯ eating quickly
- ◯ taking small bites

4 Nick is carrying a <u>bouquet</u>.
- ◯ bunch of flowers
- ◯ type of backpack
- ◯ large box
- ◯ bowl of food

5 This kind of bird <u>soars</u>.
- ◯ does not fly
- ◯ flies high in the air
- ◯ hurts or aches
- ◯ has large wings

6 <u>Swallow</u> before you talk.
- ◯ type of small brown bird
- ◯ think about what to say
- ◯ make food go down your throat
- ◯ take something out of your mouth

7 Let's walk to the <u>pier</u>.
- ◯ platform over water
- ◯ beach with boats
- ◯ sweet fruit
- ◯ small bridge

3   Copyright © Pearson Education, Inc., or its affiliates. All Rights Reserved.

GO ON

PHONICS

Directions

Find the word or words that best answer each question. Fill in the circle next to the answer.

8 I <u>ate</u> an apple.

Which word sounds the same as <u>ate</u>?

- ○ eight
- ○ at
- ○ eat
- ○ oat

9 Come over <u>here</u>!

Which word sounds the same as <u>here</u>?

- ○ hair
- ○ hire
- ○ hear
- ○ her

10 We finished our project in a <u>week</u>.

Which word sounds the same as <u>week</u>?

- ○ wreck
- ○ weak
- ○ wick
- ○ which

11 Gab's mother told him not to <u>stare</u>.

Which word sounds the same as <u>stare</u>?

- ○ star
- ○ store
- ○ steer
- ○ stair

12 The last answer was marked <u>right</u>.

Which word sounds the same as <u>right</u>?

- ○ ring
- ○ rigged
- ○ write
- ○ wire

COMPREHENSION

At the Top

There are eight different kinds of bears spread across the Earth. They live in different habitats and eat different things. One of the best types of bear is the polar bear.

Polar bears live in the Arctic. The Arctic is a cold, icy area that covers most northern parts of the Earth. Polar bears are interesting animals because they can live in such a remote part of the world.

3 Copyright © Pearson Education, Inc., or its affiliates. All Rights Reserved.

GO ON

Polar bear babies, called cubs, weigh about as much as a large book. But they can grow to weigh twice as much as a tiger! But polar bears are better than tigers.

Polar bears were built for living in the cold. They have thick, fatty blubber and a lot of fur to keep them warm. Each strand of a polar bear's fur is hollow. You can see through it!

One of the most interesting things about polar bears is the way they look. Polar bears are usually white or cream colored. This protects them because they are hard to see against the white snow and ice. You might think polar bears have white skin too, but it is actually black. Like many animals in the Arctic, they have a short tail and small ears that don't get cold.

Polar bears also have small heads and long bodies, which help them swim. They spend a lot of time in the water. They are very good swimmers, which makes them special. All the fat on their bodies helps them float.

Polar bears also spend time on ice and on land. Polar bears are one of the world's largest carnivores that live on land. A carnivore is an animal that eats other animals. Polar bears eat seals, walruses, and whales. But you don't have to be afraid of polar bears because most people only see them in zoos.

Directions
Choose the item that best answers each question about the selection you just read. Fill in the circle next to the answer.

Copyright © Pearson Education, Inc., or its affiliates. All Rights Reserved. 3

13 What detail from the selection supports the idea that polar bears are interesting animals?

○ Most people only see polar bears in the zoo.

○ Polar bears have a lot of fur to help keep them warm.

○ Adult polar bears spend a lot of time in the water.

○ Polar bears can survive in a remote part of the world.

14 Which detail from the selection supports the idea that polar bears are good swimmers?

○ Polar bears have small heads and long bodies.

○ Polar bears have hollow fur that you can see through.

○ Polar bears spend time on ice and land.

○ Polar bears have black skin.

GO ON

15 Compared to tigers, adult polar bears

- ○ are smaller.
- ○ weigh more.
- ○ eat more.
- ○ grow faster.

16 Which detail from the selection supports the idea that polar bears are built for living in the cold?

- ○ Polar bears are usually white or cream colored.
- ○ Polar bears have a short tail and small ears.
- ○ Polar bear cubs weigh about as much as a large book.
- ○ Polar bears are one of the world's largest carnivores on land.

17 Which detail about polar bears is not found in the selection?

- ○ Polar bears eat seals, walruses, and whales.
- ○ Polar bears live in the cold, icy Arctic.
- ○ Polar bears have less food because of melting ice.
- ○ Polar bears have thick, fatty blubber.

18 What is an effect of polar bears' having fat on their bodies?

- ○ It makes them cold.
- ○ It helps them run.
- ○ It helps them float.
- ○ It makes them look white.

19 What conclusion can you draw from paragraph 7?

- ○ Polar bears eat plants and animals.
- ○ Polar bears eat a lot of meat.
- ○ Polar bears eat people.
- ○ Many other animals are larger than polar bears.

20 What is the topic of this selection?

- ○ animals that live in the Arctic cold
- ○ why polar bears are interesting
- ○ eight kinds of bears
- ○ different types of Arctic habitats

3 Copyright © Pearson Education, Inc., or its affiliates. All Rights Reserved.

WRITTEN RESPONSE TO THE SELECTION

Look Back and Write Look back at the question on page 231. How are the girl's two sets of grandparents alike? How are they different? Use information from the selection to write about how they each celebrate their culture. Provide evidence to support your answer.

The information in the box below will help you remember what you should think about when you write your composition.

REMEMBER—YOU SHOULD

☐   explain how the girl's two sets of grandparents are alike and different.

☐   organize the ways the grandparents are alike in your composition and then organize the ways they are different.

☐   write about your ideas in detail so that the reader really understands what you are saying.

☐   try to use correct spelling, capitalization, punctuation, grammar, and sentences.

3 Copyright © Pearson Education, Inc., or its affiliates. All Rights Reserved.

3 Copyright © Pearson Education, Inc., or its affiliates. All Rights Reserved.

VOCABULARY

Directions

Find the word or words with the same meaning as the underlined word. Fill in the circle next to the answer.

1 <u>Raindrops</u> hit the window.

- ○ sand from the beach
- ○ leaves from trees
- ○ water from clouds
- ○ grass from the mower

2 James wished his friend <u>farewell</u>.

- ○ delicious
- ○ thank you
- ○ good-bye
- ○ homesick

3 The <u>airport</u> is a busy place.

- ○ place for parking trucks
- ○ place for loading ships
- ○ place for boarding trains
- ○ place for landing planes

4 We will always have our <u>memories</u>.

- ○ things that are remembered
- ○ things that are bought
- ○ things that are created
- ○ things that are important

5 Kim <u>described</u> her shoes.

- ○ cleaned up
- ○ searched for
- ○ gave away
- ○ told about

6 The <u>curious</u> kitten got into trouble.

- ○ wanting to know
- ○ wanting to play
- ○ wanting to sleep
- ○ wanting to eat

7 We stacked the wooden boards in the <u>cellar</u>.

- ○ attic
- ○ kitchen cupboard
- ○ basement
- ○ garage

GO ON

3 Copyright © Pearson Education, Inc., or its affiliates. All Rights Reserved.

PHONICS

*D*irections

Find the word or words that best answer each question. Fill in the circle next to the answer.

8 Lauren is their <u>daughter</u>.

Which word has the same sound as the <u>augh</u> in <u>daughter</u>?

○ laugh
○ bounce
○ talk
○ plow

9 The eggs were <u>brought</u> to the farmer's market.

Which word has the same sound as the <u>ough</u> in <u>brought</u>?

○ mall
○ hour
○ ocean
○ round

10 It wasn't my <u>fault</u>.

Which word has the same sound as the <u>au</u> in <u>fault</u>?

○ fell
○ drawn
○ fear
○ volt

11 Wanda wants to be an <u>author</u> when she's older.

Which word has the same sound as the <u>au</u> in <u>author</u>?

○ wall
○ toll
○ note
○ ounce

12 Is the statement true or <u>false</u>?

Which word has the same sound as the <u>a</u> in <u>false</u>?

○ cats
○ sale
○ fail
○ saw

COMPREHENSION

Goal!

Chelsea was jogging through the park when she saw a group of kids playing soccer and stopped to watch the game. There was an uneven number of players, so Chelsea decided to take a risk and ran forward.

3 Copyright © Pearson Education, Inc., or its affiliates. All Rights Reserved.

"Can I join your game?" she called breathlessly, as the playing stopped and everyone looked at her.

"I'm Andrew. I recognize you from school," a boy said.

"We don't need anyone else," a redheaded boy growled, kicking the ball.

"We're a player short," Andrew said. "What position do you play?"

"Forward," Chelsea said and ran out onto the field. Unfortunately, Chelsea was facing the redheaded boy when they lined up to start playing.

"Nobody asked you to play," the boy sneered. Just then, Andrew kicked the ball and there was no time to respond. Chelsea took off toward the goal. She was glad to see the redheaded boy's surprise when she sprinted past him. She played soccer on a league after school and could outrun the rest of her team.

Andrew dribbled down the field and passed the ball to another teammate to get past the defense. When the teammate passed the ball to Chelsea, she was there to sink it easily into the goal. Her team cheered.

"I guess you're pretty good," the redheaded boy grumbled as Andrew gave her a high-five.

"You should play with us every week!" Andrew said.

"I've got to get home now," Chelsea said. "But I'll definitely be back!"

Directions
Choose the item that best answers each question about the selection you just read. Fill in the circle next to the answer.

13 What conclusion does Chelsea draw in paragraph 1?

○ The team needs another player.
○ The team wants her to play.
○ The redheaded boy does not want her to play.
○ She knows Andrew from school.

14 After Chelsea interrupts the game, which event happens next?

○ Chelsea says she plays the forward position.
○ Andrew introduces himself.
○ The redheaded boy says they don't need anyone else.
○ Andrew kicks the ball.

3 Copyright © Pearson Education, Inc., or its affiliates. All Rights Reserved.

15 Which of the following events happens first?

○ Chelsea takes off toward the goal.

○ The teams line up to start playing.

○ Chelsea sinks the ball into the goal.

○ Chelsea runs out onto the field.

16 What can you infer about the redheaded boy in paragraph 4?

○ He does not want Chelsea to play.

○ He wants Chelsea to play on his team.

○ He is jealous that Chelsea is a better player than he is.

○ He recognizes Chelsea from school.

17 Which event happens before Chelsea's team cheers?

○ The redheaded boy tells her she's pretty good.

○ A teammate gets the ball past the defense.

○ Chelsea goes home.

○ Andrew tells her she should play every week.

18 Compared to Andrew, the redheaded boy

○ is nicer to Chelsea.

○ is a better soccer player.

○ is more talkative.

○ is mean to Chelsea.

19 Which of the following events happens after Chelsea makes the goal?

○ Chelsea sprints past the redheaded boy.

○ Andrew dribbles the ball down the field.

○ Andrew gives her a high-five.

○ The playing stops and everyone looks at her.

20 What can you infer about the plot's final resolution?

○ The redheaded boy will respect Chelsea's ability.

○ Andrew will not let Chelsea play on his team again.

○ Chelsea's parents will be angry that she is late for dinner.

○ Chelsea will quit playing on the soccer league after school.

3 Copyright © Pearson Education, Inc., or its affiliates. All Rights Reserved.

GO ON

WRITTEN RESPONSE TO THE SELECTION

Look Back and Write Look back at the question on page 263. Think about Jangmi's life at 382 Shin Dang Dong. Now write a paragraph telling why she might have a hard time adapting to a new culture. Provide evidence to support your answer.

The information in the box below will help you remember what you should think about when you write your composition.

REMEMBER—YOU SHOULD

☐ explain why Jangmi might have a hard time adapting to a new culture.

☐ make sure you support your answer with different details from the story.

☐ write your composition in your own words.

☐ try to use correct spelling, capitalization, punctuation, grammar, and sentences.

3 Copyright © Pearson Education, Inc., or its affiliates. All Rights Reserved.

3 Copyright © Pearson Education, Inc., or its affiliates. All Rights Reserved.

VOCABULARY

Directions
Find the word or words with the same meaning as the underlined word. Fill in the circle next to the answer.

1 Uncle Ray works in a **bakery**.

- ⃝ a store that sells meat
- ⃝ a store that sells flowers
- ⃝ a store that sells baked goods
- ⃝ a store that sells fresh fruit

2 Do we have all the **ingredients**?

- ⃝ tools
- ⃝ books
- ⃝ pencils
- ⃝ materials

3 Put the **dough** in the pan.

- ⃝ dry powder used to make milk
- ⃝ hot water used to make soup
- ⃝ sticky mixture used to make bread
- ⃝ chopped vegetables used to make stew

4 The next **batch** is almost ready.

- ⃝ group
- ⃝ train
- ⃝ band
- ⃝ meal

5 Michelle is known for her **braided** hair.

- ⃝ curled
- ⃝ brushed back
- ⃝ washed
- ⃝ woven together

6 Mama heated the **mixture**.

- ⃝ things blended together
- ⃝ pot filled with water
- ⃝ large pan
- ⃝ coal stove

7 Wait until the milk **boils**.

- ⃝ is stirred until it is mixed
- ⃝ is heated until it is bubbling
- ⃝ is stored until it is needed
- ⃝ is used until it is gone

GO ON

3 Copyright © Pearson Education, Inc., or its affiliates. All Rights Reserved.

PHONICS

Directions

Find the word or words that best answer each question. Fill in the circle next to the answer.

8 She is <u>eight</u> years old.

Which word has the same sound as the eigh in <u>eight</u>?

- ○ they
- ○ sigh
- ○ height
- ○ shoe

9 Are <u>reindeer</u> real animals?

Which word has the same sound as the <u>ei</u> in <u>reindeer</u>?

- ○ teach
- ○ bread
- ○ prey
- ○ either

10 The bride wore a <u>veil</u>.

Which word has the same sound as the <u>ei</u> in <u>veil</u>?

- ○ seed
- ○ insane
- ○ beat
- ○ neither

11 He <u>weighs</u> ninety pounds.

Which word has the same sound as the eigh in <u>weighs</u>?

- ○ there
- ○ sigh
- ○ cough
- ○ play

12 I can see <u>veins</u> in my arm.

Which word has the same sound as the <u>ei</u> in <u>veins</u>?

- ○ self
- ○ might
- ○ seat
- ○ main

3 Copyright © Pearson Education, Inc., or its affiliates. All Rights Reserved.

GO ON

COMPREHENSION

Calling All Chefs

Maria had always wanted to be a chef. She helped her parents in the kitchen and offered new ideas for recipes. She roasted vegetables for her father's plain lasagna. She added fruit and nuts to her mother's salad. When she helped her grandmother add spices to pasta sauce, everyone ate second helpings.

"I don't know how you do it," her grandmother said, smelling the bubbling sauce. "Everything you make is delicious!"

Some people thought cooking was boring. But Maria thought of cooking as an art. She wanted to make the flavors just right. And when the colors on the plate went together, the food actually seemed to taste better.

One day, Maria's mother came home from work holding a piece of paper. Surprise twinkled in her eyes.

"What's this?" Maria asked, taking the paper from her mother. "Calling all chefs?"

"The school district is sponsoring a cooking competition," her mother explained. "I saw the flyer today. Maria, you have to enter!"

"I don't know," said Maria. "The other chefs will be really good."

"You're really good!" Maria's mother said. "And you love to cook. You can come to the supermarket with me and pick out the ingredients. Grandma and I will help you chop and use the stove, but you will be the head chef."

Maria spent all night thinking about the competition. At school, she made notes about possible recipes. Finally she decided on the perfect dish.

"We need corn, beans, sweet plantains, and lime," she told her mother as they drove to the store.

"I know this is going to be delicious," her mother said. "I hope you make enough so that we can all have some, not just the judges at the competition."

3 Copyright © Pearson Education, Inc., or its affiliates. All Rights Reserved.

GO ON

COMPREHENSION

Directions

Choose the item that best answers each question about the selection you just read.
Fill in the circle next to the answer.

13 What conclusion can you draw from paragraph 1?

○ Maria's parents are not good cooks.

○ Maria needs help cooking.

○ Maria is a good cook.

○ People don't like Maria's cooking.

14 What inference can you make in paragraph 2?

○ The sauce smells good.

○ The sauce is too hot.

○ Maria's grandmother doesn't know how to make sauce.

○ Maria didn't help make the sauce.

15 Based on paragraph 3, compared to Maria, some people

○ are better cooks.

○ also like to cook.

○ think cooking is an art.

○ are not interested in cooking.

16 What happens next after Maria takes notes on possible recipes?

○ Maria tells her mother what ingredients she needs.

○ Her mother urges Maria to enter the cooking competition.

○ Maria decides on the perfect dish to cook.

○ Her mother goes shopping for ingredients.

17 What detail lets you draw the conclusion that Maria will enter the competition?

○ She loves to cook.

○ She spends all night thinking about the competition.

○ She says the other chefs will be good.

○ She says she doesn't know.

18 What happens in the plot of the story in paragraph 10?

○ Maria and her mother drive to the supermarket.

○ Maria buys the food she needs.

○ Maria thinks about entering the competition.

○ Maria cooks the food for the competition.

19 What can you infer about Maria's mother in paragraph 11?

○ She wants Maria to win the competition.

○ She will not help Maria prepare the meal.

○ She does not like competitions.

○ She enjoys eating Maria's food.

20 What conclusion can you draw about Maria's family?

○ They do not like to cook as much as other people.

○ They don't like to eat Maria's food.

○ They support Maria's love of cooking.

○ They are more competitive than everyone else.

3 Copyright © Pearson Education, Inc., or its affiliates. All Rights Reserved.

WRITTEN RESPONSE TO THE SELECTION

Look Back and Write Look back through the story. Think about the two cultures of Pablo's parents. Now write a paragraph telling why jalapeño bagels are special to Pablo. Be sure to include facts and details from the story in your paragraph.

The information in the box below will help you remember what you should think about when you write your composition.

REMEMBER—YOU SHOULD

☐ explain why jalapeño bagels are special to Pablo.

☐ include details about both Pablo's mother and father in your writing.

☐ sum up your answer in the final sentence of your paragraph.

☐ try to use correct spelling, capitalization, punctuation, grammar, and sentences.

 3 Copyright © Pearson Education, Inc., or its affiliates. All Rights Reserved.

GO ON

3 Copyright © Pearson Education, Inc., or its affiliates. All Rights Reserved.

VOCABULARY

Directions
Find the word or words with the same meaning as the underlined word. Fill in the circle next to the answer.

1 A <u>fierce</u> wind blew across the plains.
- ○ quiet
- ○ cold
- ○ strong
- ○ sudden

2 The box was made from <u>cardboard</u>.
- ○ colored plates of glass
- ○ strong sheets of plastic
- ○ thick, stiff pieces of paper
- ○ long, thin strips of metal

3 Deena <u>ruined</u> her picture.
- ○ admired
- ○ presented
- ○ framed
- ○ spoiled

4 Aunt Bess made a <u>feast</u>.
- ○ huge meal
- ○ new dress
- ○ flower pot
- ○ model car

5 The boys <u>treasure</u> their tree house.
- ○ broke
- ○ lost
- ○ dislike
- ○ value

6 We sat on the <u>stoops</u>.
- ○ front steps
- ○ metal chairs
- ○ park benches
- ○ picnic tables

7 The crowd cheered for the <u>pitcher</u>.
- ○ football team
- ○ flights
- ○ baseball player
- ○ town hero

3 Copyright © Pearson Education, Inc., or its affiliates. All Rights Reserved.

WORD ANALYSIS

Directions
Find the suffix in the underlined word. Fill in the circle next to the answer.

8 The clown is acting <u>foolish</u>.
- ○ sh
- ○ ish
- ○ lish
- ○ fool

9 Daisy had fun in her <u>childhood</u>.
- ○ hood
- ○ od
- ○ ood
- ○ child

10 That bread is <u>chewy</u>.
- ○ ch
- ○ chew
- ○ wy
- ○ y

11 The band added <u>enjoyment</u> to the event.
- ○ enjoy
- ○ ent
- ○ ment
- ○ en

12 Josie is very <u>ticklish</u>.
- ○ tick
- ○ sh
- ○ ish
- ○ lish

COMPREHENSION

Positive Video Games

Young people spend so much time playing video games that many parents are worried about the effects.

Some say video games are harmful to young minds. Others say that video games cause violence. Still others claim that video games distract kids from their schoolwork. But most of what people say about video games is false. People who are against video games do not understand them. Video games are healthy for young people.

Video games don't make kids violent. Instead, video games help kids learn how to behave in society. Most young gamers are not violent. Besides, young people enjoy many kinds of games—including puzzle games, sports games, and simulation games.

3 Copyright © Pearson Education, Inc., or its affiliates. All Rights Reserved.

GO ON

In the past, kids used dolls and action figures as a way to play make-believe. Today, video games teach similar skills. Playing video games, kids learn about cause and effect, rules, and right and wrong. Gaming offers young people a chance to explore their values. Young people who are aware of their values are more prepared for life in the real world.

Furthermore, video games do not cause young people to lose communication skills. Instead, they teach the importance of teamwork. Because many games are designed to be played by more than one player, kids play against friends and family. This helps them learn about healthy competition. They also learn how to work together to overcome challenges.

Finally, video games teach problem-solving skills. Since games make young people comfortable with computers, they are more likely to be comfortable using other, more complex types of technology. Meanwhile, as young people play video games, they are always looking for creative solutions to problems. There are usually several ways to advance to the next level in a video game. As they play the same game again and again, kids are learning a valuable lesson: not to give up.

If more parents would sit down with their kids, pick up the controller, and push the start button, they too would understand that video games are educational—and fun.

Directions
Choose the item that best answers each question about the selection you just read. Fill in the circle next to the answer.

13 **In paragraphs 1 and 2, the author introduces the topic by explaining that**

○ what people say about video games is false.

○ video games cause violence in young people.

○ video games are harmful to young minds.

○ video games distract kids from their schoolwork.

14 **The author of the selection is trying to persuade the reader that**

○ video games are expensive.

○ video games are a waste of time.

○ video games are harmful.

○ video games are healthy.

3 Copyright © Pearson Education, Inc., or its affiliates. All Rights Reserved.

15 In paragraph 3, which statement does the author use to prove that video games do not make young people violent?

○ Violent video games should only be played by parents.

○ Sports games are more popular than violent games.

○ Most young gamers are not violent.

○ Violent video games prepare young people for the real world.

16 What is the author's purpose for discussing dolls and action figures in paragraph 4?

○ to explain that dolls and action figures are now boring

○ to explain that video games teach similar skills

○ to explain that video games are better than action figures

○ to explain the dolls prepare kids for the real world

17 What conclusion can you draw from paragraph 5?

○ Young people often fight over video games.

○ Puzzle games are the most educational.

○ Most kids play video games alone.

○ Working together is part of playing video games.

18 Which detail in paragraph 6 supports the idea that video games teach problem-solving?

○ Young people often throw things at the video screen.

○ Young players search for creative solutions.

○ Video games often involve complex technology.

○ Young people play the same game again and again.

19 What is one effect of young people's being comfortable with computers?

○ They are likely to ignore their homework in favor of video games.

○ They are likely to become professional computer programmers.

○ They are likely to be comfortable with complex technology.

○ They are likely to spend all their time in front of the computer.

20 What is the author's purpose in paragraph 7?

○ to encourage parents to play video games with their kids

○ to describe different types of educational games

○ to recommend that kids play with dolls and action figures

○ to explain that video games make kids happy

3 Copyright © Pearson Education, Inc., or its affiliates. All Rights Reserved.

GO ON

WRITTEN RESPONSE TO THE SELECTION

> **Look Back and Write** Look back at the adventures James had in New York City. Now write about why you would or would not like to visit Uncle Romie in Harlem. Provide evidence to support your answer.

The information in the box below will help you remember what you should think about when you write your composition.

REMEMBER—YOU SHOULD

☐ explain why you would or would not like to visit James's Uncle Romie in Harlem.

☐ make sure you pick relevant details from the story that support your answer.

☐ imagine yourself in James's place as you write.

☐ try to use correct spelling, capitalization, punctuation, grammar, and sentences.

---

3 Copyright © Pearson Education, Inc., or its affiliates. All Rights Reserved.

3 Copyright © Pearson Education, Inc., or its affiliates. All Rights Reserved.

VOCABULARY

Directions

Find the word or words with the same meaning as the underlined word. Fill in the circle next to the answer.

1 Brad <u>unveiled</u> his painting.

- ○ untied
- ○ unloaded
- ○ uncovered
- ○ unlocked

2 The party was <u>unforgettable</u>.

- ○ to be forgotten again
- ○ easily forgotten
- ○ not to be forgotten
- ○ able to be forgotten

3 Grandpa held the <u>torch</u>.

- ○ ice cream
- ○ garden hose
- ○ light bulb
- ○ burning light

4 We read the words on the <u>tablet</u>.

- ○ flat surface for writing
- ○ wooden post
- ○ cardboard box
- ○ metal sign

5 Daria wore a <u>crown</u>.

- ○ silver gown
- ○ gold bracelet
- ○ silk robe
- ○ royal head covering

6 The ship <u>models</u> are on the table.

- ○ small copies
- ○ ink drawings
- ○ plastic containers
- ○ large plates

7 Our flag stands for <u>liberty</u>.

- ○ symbol
- ○ peace
- ○ freedom
- ○ courage

GO ON

3 Copyright © Pearson Education, Inc., or its affiliates. All Rights Reserved.

PHONICS

Directions

Find the word that best answers each question. Fill in the circle next to the answer.

8 Alice has a loose <u>tooth</u>.

Which word has the same sound as
<u>oo</u> in <u>tooth</u>?

- ○ look
- ○ glue
- ○ teeth
- ○ toy

9 My bike is red and <u>blue</u>.

Which word has the same sound as
<u>ue</u> in <u>blue</u>?

- ○ black
- ○ blow
- ○ letter
- ○ booth

10 The table is made of <u>wood</u>.

Which word has the same sound as
<u>oo</u> in <u>wood</u>?

- ○ was
- ○ suit
- ○ bush
- ○ bamboo

11 Lan <u>put</u> the book on the shelf.

Which word has the same sound as
<u>u</u> in <u>put</u>?

- ○ took
- ○ pop
- ○ blew
- ○ fruit

12 We like to drink orange <u>juice</u>.

Which word has the same sound as
<u>ui</u> in <u>juice</u>?

- ○ fool
- ○ ice
- ○ jump
- ○ jolly

COMPREHENSION

The Strange Story of the Umbrella

When it rains, most people take out an umbrella to stay dry. But this was not always
the case. For thousands of years, umbrellas were only used to protect people from the sun's
rays, not rain. The word *umbrella* comes from a Latin word meaning "shade."

The umbrella was invented in Mesopotamia in the Middle East about 3,500 years ago.
In ancient Egypt umbrellas were only used by kings, queens, and other nobles. A
servant would carry the umbrella and hold it over the noble's head. This would

GO ON

3 Copyright © Pearson Education, Inc., or its affiliates. All Rights Reserved.

protect the royal person from being burned by the scorching sun. An umbrella became a symbol of royalty. Today some chiefs in African countries still use umbrellas this way.

The ancient Greeks used umbrellas too. They may have been the first people to use them to protect themselves from rain. They oiled the surface of the umbrella to make it waterproof. But only women used the umbrellas. Greek men thought umbrellas were for wimps.

For hundreds of years umbrellas continued to be used only by women. Then, in the 1700s, that changed. A wealthy man in England named Jonas Hanway liked the umbrella. He thought everyone should use it to stay dry on a rainy day. He carried his umbrella with him wherever he went.

People would see Hanway on the street with his umbrella and laugh. They thought he was slightly mad. "No man should be seen with an umbrella," they said. "They are only for women." But Hanway was stubborn. He continued to carry his umbrella. He did so for thirty years.

People started to think that maybe Hanway wasn't so crazy after all. They saw that he stayed dry in a rainstorm when other men got wet. Their only way to get out of the rain was to run for a building or hail a carriage. Soon men in England changed their minds about umbrellas. Everyone began to use them. They even called them *Hanways* in honor of Jonas Hanway.

Next time you open your umbrella on a rainy day, give a thought to the man who made it possible—Jonas Hanway.

Directions

Choose the item that best answers each question about the selection you just read. Fill in the circle next to the answer.

13 **What is the main idea of paragraph 2?**
- ◯ The umbrella was invented 3,500 years ago.
- ◯ Umbrellas were first used to protect people from the sun.
- ◯ Only royalty used early umbrellas.
- ◯ Umbrellas have been popular for a long time.

14 **What conclusion can you draw from the facts in paragraph 2?**
- ◯ Noble people did not have sunburn.
- ◯ It never rained in ancient Egypt.
- ◯ 3,500 years ago, umbrellas were heavier.
- ◯ Mesopotamia was always cloudy.

3 Copyright © Pearson Education, Inc., or its affiliates. All Rights Reserved.

15 **What is the topic of the selection?**

○ the life of Jonas Hanway

○ why umbrellas are healthy

○ the history of the umbrella

○ umbrellas in ancient times

16 **What opinion did Greek men have of umbrellas?**

○ Oil was a smart way to make things waterproof.

○ Protecting themselves from the rain was not manly.

○ Their umbrellas were better than Egyptian umbrellas.

○ Greek women looked lovely carrying umbrellas.

17 **What opinion did the English people *first* have of Jonas Hanway?**

○ They thought he needed an umbrella.

○ They thought he was too rich.

○ They thought he was ahead of his time.

○ They thought he was crazy.

18 **Which generalization is true according to the selection?**

○ Umbrellas are the greatest invention of all time.

○ Only women used umbrellas for a long time.

○ All umbrellas are used to protect people from rain.

○ Englishmen always carried umbrellas in the rain.

19 **What conclusion can you draw from the facts about Jonas Hanway?**

○ He often forgot his umbrella at home.

○ He wanted umbrellas to be named after him.

○ He sewed his own umbrellas.

○ He didn't care what other people thought.

20 **Opinions about umbrellas have changed over time because today**

○ both men and women use umbrellas.

○ only men use umbrellas as protection from the rain.

○ only royalty use umbrellas.

○ umbrellas are used only as protection from the sun.

3 Copyright © Pearson Education, Inc., or its affiliates. All Rights Reserved.

GO ON

WRITTEN RESPONSE TO THE SELECTION

Look Back and Write Look back through the story to find what is interesting or important about the Statue of Liberty. Write a paragraph using facts and details to support this idea.

The information in the box below will help you remember what you should think about when you write your composition.

REMEMBER—YOU SHOULD

☐ explain what is interesting or important about the Statue of Liberty.

☐ make sure you choose the most interesting and important details for your paragraph.

☐ organize your ideas.

☐ try to use correct spelling, capitalization, punctuation, grammar, and sentences.

3 Copyright © Pearson Education, Inc., or its affiliates. All Rights Reserved.

_____

_____

_____

_____

_____

_____

_____

_____

_____

_____

_____

_____

_____

_____

_____

_____

_____

3 Copyright © Pearson Education, Inc., or its affiliates. All Rights Reserved.

VOCABULARY

Directions

Find the word or words with the same meaning as the underlined word. Fill in the circle next to the answer.

1 I use my grandmother's <u>recipe</u>.

- ◯ wooden chair
- ◯ knitting needles
- ◯ cooking directions
- ◯ feather pillow

2 Chin came from a <u>foreign</u> country.

- ◯ large
- ◯ cold
- ◯ different
- ◯ friendly

3 The boy was acting <u>foolish</u>.

- ◯ famous
- ◯ greedy
- ◯ eager
- ◯ silly

4 Randy's bird <u>perches</u> on the windowsill.

- ◯ sits
- ◯ drinks
- ◯ climbs
- ◯ scratches

5 Dad wore a <u>narrow</u> tie.

- ◯ silk
- ◯ colorful
- ◯ woven
- ◯ slim

6 The weather outside was <u>chilly</u>.

- ◯ cold
- ◯ warm
- ◯ hot
- ◯ dry

7 The actor <u>bows</u> to the audience.

- ◯ speaks
- ◯ performs
- ◯ bends forward
- ◯ plays

3 Copyright © Pearson Education, Inc., or its affiliates. All Rights Reserved.

GO ON

PHONICS

Directions

For each underlined word, choose the item that shows how to divide it correctly into syllables. Fill in the circle next to the answer.

8 The airplane flew <u>above</u> the clouds.

- ○ a | bove
- ○ ab | ove
- ○ abo | ve
- ○ abov | e

9 You can't buy much for a <u>nickel</u>.

- ○ ni | ckel
- ○ nic | kel
- ○ nick | el
- ○ nicke | l

10 Joe borrowed a cup of <u>sugar</u>.

- ○ su | gar
- ○ sug | ar
- ○ suga | r
- ○ s | ugar

11 Sue is <u>afraid</u> of the dark.

- ○ af | raid
- ○ afra | id
- ○ afr | aid
- ○ a | fraid

12 The museum had a <u>dinosaur</u> exhibit.

- ○ din | o | saur
- ○ di | no | saur
- ○ d | ino | saur
- ○ dino | saur

3 Copyright © Pearson Education, Inc., or its affiliates. All Rights Reserved.

GO ON

COMPREHENSION

Ralph's Starring Role

Ralph had never been so nervous in all his life. The school play was about to begin, and Ralph had a starring role in it. Actually, he was playing a star. Other students were playing the roles of different heavenly bodies. The play was called "A Journey to Jupiter." The stars and planets were characters in the play. And they all had lines they had to memorize.

Ralph had never acted on stage before. He only auditioned for the play because his friend and classmate Bart was auditioning. Bart got the role of Earth's nearest neighbor, the moon. It was a tremendous part with lots of stirring speeches. Ralph was thrilled to have a small part with just a couple of lines. He kept repeating them over and over in his head so he wouldn't forget them.

The play was about to start. The director prompted the actors to get on stage and take their places. Ralph put on his pointy star costume. Now he truly looked like a member of a stellar cast! He took his place and waited for the curtain to rise and for the play to get underway. A rocket ship traveling to Jupiter appeared. It rolled across the stage on wheels. A girl peered out from inside the rocket ship. "Wow!" she said. "Look at all the brilliant stars!"

That was Ralph's cue. Ralph was supposed to say, "Hi! Where are you going?" But he was so nervous that he couldn't remember his line. All he could remember was "Hi!"

The girl frowned at him. "We're going to Jupiter," she said. "Do you know how to get there?" She was afraid that Ralph would forget the next line too. But he remembered it.

"Just go past Saturn with all its rings, and Jupiter is straight ahead," he said.

"Thanks!" said the girl with a smile.

Ralph bowed, and the audience laughed. Ralph felt good. Maybe he'd forgotten one line, but he remembered the other one. And the audience liked him. He was a star all right!

When the play was over, all the actors took their bows. Ralph smiled and bowed again. "Well, you got through it okay," said Bart in his moon costume. "Are you still nervous?"

"Not at all," said Ralph. "This was more fun than I thought it would be. I think I'm going to try out for the next school play."

3 Copyright © Pearson Education, Inc., or its affiliates. All Rights Reserved.

GO ON

Directions

Choose the item that best answers each question about the selection you just read. Fill in the circle next to the answer.

13 What caused Ralph to be nervous?

○ He was wearing an embarrassing costume.

○ He had never acted on stage before.

○ He had a role he didn't like.

○ People were laughing at him.

14 Ralph played the role of

○ Jupiter.

○ Earth.

○ a star.

○ the moon.

15 What effect did Ralph's forgetting his line have on the other actor?

○ She forgot her next line.

○ She whispered the line to him.

○ She turned red in the face.

○ She frowned at Ralph.

16 Why did Ralph audition for the play?

○ because his friend Bart was auditioning

○ because he wanted to be a star

○ because he was bored

○ because he liked science fiction plays

17 What effect did the audience's laughing have on Ralph?

○ It made him feel good.

○ It made him more nervous.

○ It made him angry.

○ It made him feel foolish.

18 What happened when the play ended?

○ Ralph made a speech.

○ The director came on stage.

○ The actors took their bows.

○ Bart took off his costume.

19 What caused Ralph to tell Bart that he wanted to audition for the next play?

○ He wanted to get a bigger part.

○ Bart said he wouldn't audition.

○ He enjoyed being in the play.

○ He wanted to please his friend.

20 Which sentence best expresses the theme or message of the story?

○ Being in a play is hard work.

○ Trying something new can be a good experience.

○ "A Journey to Jupiter" is a funny play.

○ Some people shouldn't be on stage.

3 Copyright © Pearson Education, Inc., or its affiliates. All Rights Reserved.

GO ON

WRITTEN RESPONSE TO THE SELECTION

Look Back and Write What is special about Mr. Kang's birthday? Look back through the story and think about what Mr. Kang does during the days after his birthday. Write a response to the question, providing evidence to support your answer.

The information in the box below will help you remember what you should think about when you write your composition.

REMEMBER—YOU SHOULD

- ☐ explain what is special about Mr. Kang's birthday.

- ☐ put the events in order and use time order words.

- ☐ write about your ideas simply and clearly so that the reader understands what you are saying.

- ☐ try to use correct spelling, capitalization, punctuation, grammar, and sentences.

3 Copyright © Pearson Education, Inc., or its affiliates. All Rights Reserved.

GO ON

3 Copyright © Pearson Education, Inc., or its affiliates. All Rights Reserved.

Name _____

VOCABULARY

Directions

Find the word or words with the same meaning as the underlined word. Fill in the circle next to the answer.

1 Mr. Clark is a <u>native</u> of New York.

- ○ a type of shop manager
- ○ a schoolteacher in training
- ○ a person born at a specific place
- ○ a sick or injured person

2 The song was an <u>expression</u> of his feelings.

- ○ trip
- ○ question
- ○ statement
- ○ package

3 My grandparents <u>settled</u> in Kentucky.

- ○ read a letter
- ○ took a vacation
- ○ became rich
- ○ made a home

4 Miss Mills <u>encourages</u> her students.

- ○ urges helpfully
- ○ lectures
- ○ laughs with
- ○ is rude to

5 Can we count on your <u>support</u>?

- ○ silence
- ○ attendance
- ○ answer
- ○ help

6 My mom is very concerned about <u>social</u> issues.

- ○ people and community
- ○ math and science
- ○ private and personal
- ○ radio and television

7 These vegetables come from <u>local</u> gardens.

- ○ splendid
- ○ delicate
- ○ nearby
- ○ famous

GO ON

3 Copyright © Pearson Education, Inc., or its affiliates. All Rights Reserved.

PHONICS

Directions

For each underlined word, choose the item that shows how to divide it correctly into syllables. Fill in the circle next to the answer.

8 The artist painted a new <u>picture</u>.

  ○ pict | ure
  ○ pic | ture
  ○ pi | cture
  ○ pictu |re

9 I hadn't heard that <u>expression</u> before.

  ○ ex | press | ion
  ○ ex | pres | sion
  ○ ex | pre | ssion
  ○ exp | ress | ion

10 The teacher asked the class a <u>question</u>.

  ○ qu | estion
  ○ que | stion
  ○ quest | ion
  ○ ques | tion

11 That office bulding is a tall <u>structure</u>.

  ○ struc | ture
  ○ struct | ure
  ○ stru | cture
  ○ str | uc | ture

12 Eating turkey on Thanksgiving is an American <u>tradition</u>.

  ○ trad | it | ion
  ○ tra | dition
  ○ tra | di | tion
  ○ trad | ition

COMPREHENSION

Planting a Vegetable Garden

There is nothing better—or environmentally smarter—than growing and eating your own vegetables. But before you just throw seeds into the wind, think about the following five points:

1. Soil

First of all, you must find out what type of soil you have, whether it's clay, sand, or *sandy loam*. Sandy loam is ideal. It consists of sand, silt, and clay in equal amounts. If your soil has too much sand or clay, you will have to improve the soil with *compost*. Compost is helpful to soil because it holds water and minerals.

GO ON

3 Copyright © Pearson Education, Inc., or its affiliates. All Rights Reserved.

2. Design

A good garden plan is important for beginning gardeners. Locate the garden away from buildings and trees. Make sure you find a spot with as much sun as possible. Also, start small. Beginners can get discouraged if they plant a garden that is too large to take care of.

3. Planting

Be sure to select types of vegetables that will grow well where you live. Early spring is the best time to plant. Before planting, loosen the soil to a depth of about 12 inches. Break up any clumps in the soil, remove rocks, and pull up weeds. Then make holes in the soil about half an inch deep. Drop several seeds into each hole and lightly cover the seeds with soil. You will also want to add *fertilizer* to your garden. Fertilizer helps plants grow faster by giving them the chemicals they need to succeed.

4. Pests

Protect your garden with a good fence. Squirrels, rabbits, and other animals will be very interested in eating your vegetables even before they are fully grown. For a small garden, a fence of thin wire will keep most pests away.

5. Weeds

Weeds are a fact of life in any garden, but sometimes they can take over. If weeds are growing faster than your vegetables, it's time to consider *mulch*. Mulch is any type of covering, such as grass clippings, leaves, or straw. Mulch helps keep water in the soil. Plants grow up through the mulch, but weeds are kept down.

DIRECTIONS
Choose the item that best answers each question about the selection you just read. Fill in the circle next to the answer.

13 **What opinion does the author express in paragraph 1?**

○ Growing vegetables is important to a healthy diet.

○ Growing vegetables takes a lot of hard work.

○ Growing vegetables is as easy as throwing seeds.

○ Growing vegetables is good for the environment.

14 **Compared to other types of soil, sandy loam**

○ needs compost.

○ has equal amounts of sand, silt, and clay.

○ has sand mixed in with loam.

○ holds water and minerals.

GO ON

3 Copyright © Pearson Education, Inc., or its affiliates. All Rights Reserved.

15 Under what heading would you expect to learn about seeds?

○ Soil

○ Design

○ Planting

○ Pests

16 The "Design" section has information about

○ the size and placement of a beginner garden.

○ the type of fertilizer needed for growing vegetables.

○ how to space seeds so that plants are not crowded.

○ how to use mulch to keep down weeds.

17 If the author added information about how to keep caterpillars off of plants, under which heading would you expect to find it?

○ Weeds

○ Soil

○ Design

○ Pests

18 Which of the following terms in italics in the selections gives plants the chemicals they need?

○ sandy loam

○ compost

○ fertilizer

○ mulch

19 Which of the following is the first step to planting a vegetable garden?

○ Locate the garden away from buildings and trees.

○ Select types of vegetables that will grow well.

○ Protect your garden with a good fence.

○ Find out what type of soil you have.

20 The four terms in *italics*

○ point out the only important parts of the selection.

○ highlight specific gardening terms.

○ help readers make a list to take to the garden store.

○ point out special seed types.

3 Copyright © Pearson Education, Inc., or its affiliates. All Rights Reserved.

WRITTEN RESPONSE TO THE SELECTION

Look Back and Write Look back at each artist and mural in the selection. Think about the reasons why the artists painted the murals. What do the murals represent, or stand for? Provide evidence to support your answer.

The information in the box below will help you remember what you should think about when you write your composition.

REMEMBER—YOU SHOULD

☐ explain what the murals represent, or stand for.

☐ make sure you use details from both the photographs and the text in your composition.

☐ keep your writing clear and logical.

☐ try to use correct spelling, capitalization, punctuation, grammar, and sentences.

3 Copyright © Pearson Education, Inc., or its affiliates. All Rights Reserved.

_____

_____

_____

_____

_____

_____

_____

_____

_____

_____

_____

_____

_____

_____

_____

_____

_____

_____

_____

_____

_____

_____

_____

_____

_____

_____

3 Copyright © Pearson Education, Inc., or its affiliates. All Rights Reserved.

VOCABULARY

Directions

Find the word or words with the same meaning as the underlined word. Fill in the circle next to the answer.

1 Sam read about an amazing <u>discovery</u> in space.

- ○ hero
- ○ trick
- ○ find
- ○ place

2 Daria found a <u>crystal</u> in a cave.

- ○ large white pearl
- ○ lump of gold
- ○ shiny mineral stone
- ○ chunk of clay

3 It was a long <u>journey</u>.

- ○ game
- ○ day
- ○ story
- ○ trip

4 Fred was <u>unaware</u> that he was so late.

- ○ did not know
- ○ did not worry
- ○ did not ask
- ○ did not see

5 The cat <u>disappeared</u> behind a chair.

- ○ remained
- ○ scrambled
- ○ wandered
- ○ vanished

6 The family felt <u>joyful</u> upon Harrah's return.

- ○ happy
- ○ proud
- ○ angry
- ○ upset

7 Grant needs a <u>scoop</u> of sugar for his baking project.

- ○ tall jar
- ○ round bowl
- ○ large spoon
- ○ small bag

3 Copyright © Pearson Education, Inc., or its affiliates. All Rights Reserved.

GO ON

WORD ANALYSIS

Directions

Find the word or words with the same meaning as the underlined word. Fill in the circle next to the answer.

8 The roads became <u>impassable</u> after the flood.

- ○ littered with refuse
- ○ slippery
- ○ not possible to travel over
- ○ broken down

9 Luis wants to be <u>invisible</u> so he can spy on his little brother.

- ○ cannot be seen
- ○ of great value
- ○ very tall
- ○ very smart

10 Maria was <u>impatient</u> to get her new puppy.

- ○ calmly waiting
- ○ restless and eager
- ○ unhappy
- ○ nervous

11 Leroy couldn't turn in his science project because it was <u>incomplete</u>.

- ○ left at home
- ○ someone else's work
- ○ the wrong assignment
- ○ not finished

12 It is <u>improper</u> to eat soup with a fork.

- ○ not the correct way
- ○ perfectly fine
- ○ against the law
- ○ expected

COMPREHENSION

The Squirrel Who Can't Eat Nuts

In New England, where I live, autumn is the most wonderful time of year. The leaves on the trees turn incredible colors—orange, yellow, and red. Everyone gets busy, humans and animals alike. The humans rake up all the fallen leaves, and wild animals scatter around gathering food to store for the long winter ahead.

3 Copyright © Pearson Education, Inc., or its affiliates. All Rights Reserved.

GO ON

Weekly Test 29 Unit 6 Week 4

Name _____

Two Bad Ants

I'm no wild animal. I'm a house cat called Snaggles. My humans let me spend a lot of time outdoors, though. I love it best after the yard has been raked, and I can leap and pounce all over the piles of crunchy leaves. I also love sitting in that sunny spot by the kitchen window. I can spend hours watching the outdoor animals forage for their winter food. I watch them and think how lucky I am to always know that someone will feed me!

When I get outside I enjoy talking with my squirrel friend, Wally. Now that fall is here, Wally and his family have been busy finding food to store away for hibernation. It takes Wally longer to find food than the other squirrels. My friend Wally is severely allergic to nuts.

Being allergic to nuts is quite a problem in the squirrel world. Nuts, especially acorns, are a squirrel's favorite food group. A squirrel that can't eat nuts is like a cat that can't drink milk!

Once I asked Wally what would happen if he ate a nut. He couldn't remember the last time he had one. "All I know is what my mama told me. She said that my face got swollen and that my skin got a rash. She said that I had a really bad bellyache and that they had to rush me to Dr. Owl for emergency treatment."

"But, Wally, that happened when you were just a baby. Maybe you're not allergic anymore," I said. I really liked Wally and hated to think that he was missing out on such a tasty food treat.

"Mama said I would always have this allergy and that I must never eat a nut. It's OK. There are plenty of other things I get to eat. I love bird seed and bread crumbs, and a lot of times I find treats that dogs have left outside." Yes, Wally seemed fine about the whole thing.

Still, it bothered me. I wanted Wally to enjoy nuts like all the other squirrels. One day I hid an acorn inside some bread and left it outside. Watching Wally from my window, I saw him pick it up and take a bite. I was so happy he was finally enjoying the taste of a nut! Suddenly, Wally looked like he was choking. His face got swollen, and he held his belly as if it hurt.

Luckily, Dr. Owl had been watching from high in his tree. He swooped down, picked up Wally, and gave him the emergency treatment he needed. Boy, did I learn a lesson! Even though I meant no harm, I caused a great deal of trouble for Wally and his family. I now understand how serious allergies can be, and I'm very happy that Wally has forgiven me.

GO ON

Copyright © Pearson Education, Inc., or its affiliates. All Rights Reserved.

Choose the item that best answers each question about the selection you just read. Fill in the circle next to the answer.

13 Who is narrating this story?

- ⚪ Wally the Squirrel
- ⚪ Dr. Owl
- ⚪ Snaggles the Cat
- ⚪ the human owner of a house cat

14 How does Wally deal with the problem of being a squirrel allergic to nuts?

- ⚪ He goes to Dr. Owl for allergy shots.
- ⚪ He refuses to eat and won't collect food for the winter.
- ⚪ He wants to try a nut to see if he still has the allergy.
- ⚪ He doesn't eat nuts, but there are plenty of other things to eat.

15 What does Snaggles do, thinking he is helping Wally?

- ⚪ He hides a nut in a slice of bread so that Wally will eat it.
- ⚪ He helps Wally find food that does not have any nuts.
- ⚪ He talks to Wally's mama to find out if Wally is really allergic.
- ⚪ He decides to stop drinking milk.

16 What foods can Wally enjoy eating?

- ⚪ bird seed, bread crumbs, and dog treats
- ⚪ acorns, bird seed, and bread crumbs
- ⚪ dog treats, milk, and bird seed
- ⚪ walnuts, acorns, and sesame seeds

17 What is the author's message in this story?

- ⚪ Animals can be allergic to things too.
- ⚪ Allergies can be serious.
- ⚪ Autumn is very pretty in New England.
- ⚪ House cats should not be allowed to go outside.

18 What happens after Wally takes a bite from the slice of bread Snaggles leaves outside?

- ⚪ He enjoys the taste of the nut and takes another bite.
- ⚪ He looks like he is choking, and he holds his belly.
- ⚪ Snaggles saves Wally's life.
- ⚪ Dr. Owl tells him to never eat another nut.

19 Which of the following foods would be safe for Wally to eat?

- ⚪ peanut bars
- ⚪ banana walnut bread
- ⚪ pecan pie
- ⚪ toast with jelly

20 Why does Snaggles love autumn?

- ⚪ The leaves on the trees turn incredible colors.
- ⚪ He loves raking the colorful leaves.
- ⚪ He gets busy finding food for the winter.
- ⚪ His humans give him lots of sweet treats.

3 Copyright © Pearson Education, Inc., or its affiliates. All Rights Reserved.

WRITTEN RESPONSE TO THE SELECTION

> **Look Back and Write** Look back at pages 477–479 to find "a boiling brown lake," a giant scoop," and "a cave." Write a note to tell the ants what these things really are. Provide evidence from the story to support your answer.

The information in the box below will help you remember what you should think about when you write your composition.

REMEMBER—YOU SHOULD

☐ explain to the ants what the things described on pages 477–479 are.

☐ use the pictures and text to determine for yourself what these things are before you write.

☐ use your imagination and remember you are writing to the ants in the story.

☐ try to use correct spelling, capitalization, punctuation, grammar, and sentences.

3 Copyright © Pearson Education, Inc., or its affiliates. All Rights Reserved.

3 Copyright © Pearson Education, Inc., or its affiliates. All Rights Reserved.

VOCABULARY

Directions

Find the word or words with the same meaning as the underlined word. Fill in the circle next to the answer.

1 Josh put on <u>thermal</u> mittens.

- ○ made to attract sunlight
- ○ made to prevent heat loss
- ○ brightly colored
- ○ made out of breathable fabric

2 The ceremony was to <u>honor</u> great teachers.

- ○ give a cash prize to
- ○ give speeches to
- ○ give flowers to
- ○ give formal respect to

3 We <u>crouched</u> to enter the cave.

- ○ crawled
- ○ stood on tiptoes
- ○ stood at lowered height
- ○ got on hands and knees

4 The <u>aqueducts</u> ran under the city streets.

- ○ channels for telephone wires
- ○ passages for flowing water
- ○ pipes for natural gas
- ○ tunnels for subways

5 I asked for <u>guidance</u> about my future.

- ○ predictions
- ○ advice
- ○ questions
- ○ applications

6 The porch was held up by a <u>pillar</u>.

- ○ upright support
- ○ series of steps
- ○ diagonal crossbeams
- ○ doorframe

7 Teresa was <u>content</u> with her role in the school play.

- ○ upset
- ○ pleased
- ○ angry
- ○ nervous

3 Copyright © Pearson Education, Inc., or its affiliates. All Rights Reserved.

GO ON

WORD ANALYSIS

Directions
Find the word that is related to the underlined word. Fill in the circle next to the answer.

8 When Marisa <u>dealt</u> cards to play Go Fish, each player got seven cards.

- ○ dear
- ○ deliver
- ○ deal
- ○ deaf

9 The saleswoman told us to have a <u>pleasant</u> day.

- ○ please
- ○ peasant
- ○ pheasant
- ○ playful

10 Tony has the <u>ability</u> to climb trees.

- ○ ambition
- ○ able
- ○ awareness
- ○ arm strength

11 The red <u>signal</u> means stop.

- ○ series
- ○ sing
- ○ light
- ○ sign

12 Of all the trees found in <u>nature</u>, Sylvia's favorite is the maple.

- ○ natural
- ○ nighttime
- ○ forest
- ○ narrate

COMPREHENSION

The Disastrous Party

The day of her party had finally arrived, and Beatrice was excited. The guests would be arriving any minute. She went around the house, double-checking all her preparations for the big event. In the kitchen she set out what she thought was everyone's favorite snack: water and carrot sticks.

The living room she'd decorated with pictures of tigers and other things to entertain her guests. Big pieces of paper and crayons were set out on the coffee table. Beatrice was thinking that a Drawing Contest would be enjoyable for everyone. She'd figured that everyone loved peanuts, so she'd put bowls of peanuts on every table.

GO ON

3 Copyright © Pearson Education, Inc., or its affiliates. All Rights Reserved.

The doorbell rang at exactly six o'clock, and the guests began to file in. First Beatrice took them into the kitchen for refreshments.

"That's it?" Ben asked with a frown. "Carrot sticks?"

Beatrice tried to smile. She led her guests into the living room.

"Peanuts! I'm allergic to peanuts," Marla said as she scanned the room. "If I eat peanuts, I get really sick."

"I'm sorry," Beatrice said and tried to change the subject. "I've planned a really fun thing. A Drawing Contest!"

"No fair!" exclaimed Jose. "I have a broken arm. I can't be part of a Drawing Contest."

"Don't worry," Beatrice said and took the guests into the den. "I rented an exciting movie about tigers."

"Tigers!" said Tania, "Tigers are boring!"

"Where's your phone?" Jose asked. "I'm going to call my mom and see if she'll pick me up early."

Beatrice sighed and threw herself onto the sofa. She could see that her party was a disaster. She had thought her friends would like everything she liked.

"I'm going to call my mom too," Marla said.

"Wait!" Beatrice said. "You all are my friends. I'm glad you came to my party, and I want you have a good time. I only thought about myself when I planned this party, and I should have been thinking of everyone. We can still have fun if we figure it out together. What do you guys want to do?"

Directions
Choose the item that best answers each question about the selection you just read. Fill in the circle next to the answer.

13 What generalization does Beatrice make in paragraph 1?

○ Everyone likes water and carrot sticks.
○ Everyone will be on time for the party.
○ The party will be a huge success.
○ Preparations must be double-checked.

14 What generalization does Beatrice make in paragraph 2?

○ Paper and crayons belong on the coffee table.
○ No one likes peanuts.
○ Everyone will enjoy a Drawing Contest.
○ Pictures of tigers make good decorations.

GO ON

Copyright © Pearson Education, Inc., or its affiliates. All Rights Reserved. 3

15 What fact in paragraph 4 lets you generalize that Ben does not like carrot sticks?

○ He wants to go home early.

○ He wins the Drawing Contest.

○ He eats them too quickly.

○ He frowns when he sees them.

16 What generalization can you make about Beatrice's friends?

○ They are not very polite.

○ They love Drawing Contests.

○ They enjoy watching movies.

○ They like cheeseburgers.

17 What generalization can you make about Jose in paragraph 8?

○ He is content to watch the others have the Drawing Contest.

○ He does not want the others to do anything he can't also do.

○ He is so clumsy he always has a broken arm.

○ He prefers watching movies to having Drawing Contests.

18 What conclusion can you draw from paragraph 11?

○ Jose is tired of fighting with Marla.

○ Jose is excited to watch the movie about tigers.

○ Jose has gotten sick from the peanuts.

○ Jose is not having a good time at the party.

19 By the end of the story, Beatrice has realized that

○ she should not have invited Marla and Jose.

○ she should have had a pool party.

○ she should have thought of what her friends like.

○ she should not have thrown herself onto the sofa.

20 What is the theme of this story?

○ The best way to have fun is to include everyone.

○ Many different kinds of movies make a good party.

○ The best way to plan a party is to think of yourself.

○ Many different types of food make a good party.

3 Copyright © Pearson Education, Inc., or its affiliates. All Rights Reserved.

178

WRITTEN RESPONSE TO THE SELECTION

> **Look Back and Write** Look back at pages 518–519. Talk about the reasons why the story was created. What does the story try to explain about the world? Provide evidence to support your answer.

The information in the box below will help you remember what you should think about when you write your composition.

REMEMBER—YOU SHOULD

☐   tell what the story tries to explain about the world.

☐   support each part of your answer with details from the story.

☐   organize your ideas clearly so your reader can understand them.

☐   try to use correct spelling, capitalization, punctuation, grammar, and sentences.

3 Copyright © Pearson Education, Inc., or its affiliates. All Rights Reserved.

GO ON

3 Copyright © Pearson Education, Inc., or its affiliates. All Rights Reserved.